William Dampier
in New Holland

A VOYAGE

TO

New Holland, &c.

In the Year, 1699.

Wherein are described,

The *Canary*-Islands, the Isles of *Mayo* and
St. *Jago*. The Bay of *All Saints*, with the
Forts and Town of *Bahia* in *Brasil*. Cape
Salvadore. The Winds on the *Brasilian*
Coast. *Abrohlo*-Shoals. A Table of all the
Variations observ'd in this Voyage. Oc-
currences near the Cape of *Good Hope*.
The Course to *New Holland*. *Shark*'s Bay.
The Isles and Coast, &c. of *New Holland*.

Their Inhabitants, Manners, Customs, Trade, &c.
Their Harbours, Soil, Beasts, Birds, Fish, &c.
Trees, Plants, Fruits, &c.

Illustrated with several Maps and Draughts; also
divers Birds, Fishes, and Plants, not found in
this part of the World, Curiously Ingraven on
Copper-Plates.

VOL. III.

By Captain *William Dampier*.

LONDON:

Printed for *James Knapton*, at the *Crown* in St. *Paul's*
Church-yard, 1703.

Title page of *A Voyage to New Holland* by William Dampier, 1703.

William Dampier in New Holland

AUSTRALIA'S FIRST NATURAL HISTORIAN

ALEX S. GEORGE

Bloomings Books

1999

Published by Bloomings Books

37 Burwood Road

Hawthorn Victoria 3122

Australia

National Library of Australia Cataloguing-in-Publication data:

George, Alexander S., 1939–.

William Dampier in New Holland: Australia's first natural historian.

Bibliography.

Includes index.

ISBN 1 876473 12 6.

1. Dampier, William, 1651–1715. 2. Historians of science — Australia — Biography. 3. Natural history — Australia. 4. Naturalist — Australia — Biography. I. Title.

508.092

Design: Stacey Zass, Colorperception P/L, Melbourne

Editor: Julie Stokes

Printed by Craft Print P/L

Front cover: William Dampier, a portrait painted by Thomas Murray.

An English East Indiaman similar to the *Roebuck*.

Diplolaena grandiflora.

Contents

Foreword by George Seddon   vii

Introduction   xi

Acknowledgements   xii

Notes on the text   xv

Chronology   xviii

William Dampier — natural historian, author, adventurer, privateer   1

Dampier's Australian plants   21

Dampier's Australian animals   99

Commemorating Dampier   135

Appendix: Matters of fact and opinion   145

Bibliography   151

Index   158

Foreword

George Seddon

Dampier is hardly a household name in Australia, and even in Western Australia he is much less known than the Dutch who struck the coast much further south. In 1629 Pelsaert generated a bloodthirsty melodrama. Vlamingh named the Swan River and described Rottnest Island in 1696. In 1712 the *Zuytdorp* left a 'carpet of silver' (Playford, 1996) on the sea floor south of Shark Bay. These are stories that have won some attention from the general public.

Yet Dampier visited these shores twice, in 1688 and again in 1699. The ship of his first visit, the *Cygnet*, was the first British vessel to reach the mainland coast of Australia, and the *Roebuck* voyage of 1699–1701 came close to anticipating Cook's voyage along the east coast by 70 years. The second visit was an official voyage of exploration on behalf of the British Admiralty. After sailing up the west coast of New Holland from Shark Bay to Lagrange Bay (south of Broome), he went on to Timor and rounded the northern coast of New Guinea. He had then intended to turn south to explore the east coast of New Holland but decided — given the poor state of the *Roebuck*, and uncertainty over currents and reefs — that it was prudent to head for home. He was right on both counts. Cook had trouble with the reefs, and the *Roebuck* got no further than Ascension Island in the mid-Atlantic, between Brazil and the Congo. Deciding that it was beyond repair, Dampier and his crew abandoned ship, which duly sank. They were picked up some six weeks later by a passing fleet.

Memorials to Dampier here are few, the best-known being three place names and a plant. The Dampier Archipelago (a sprinkling of basaltic islands immediately west of the Burrup Peninsula) was named in 1803 by Louis de Freycinet, Roebuck Bay by Phillip Parker King in 1821, and the modern town of Dampier was established in 1966 by Hamersley Iron (now part of Rio Tinto) as a port for exporting iron ore, the name being gazetted in 1972. The plant genus *Dampiera* was named for him in 1810 by the botanist Robert Brown. Alex George gives an exhaustive list of names as well as the handful of well-known ones in an eponymy, and he has also named a popular, spectacular and much-loved flower in his honour. The flower is Sturt's Desert Pea, but it was Dampier who first described it, not Sturt. It has had various botanical names (e.g. *Clianthus formosus, Swainsona formosa*), but George has recently given it a genus of its own — *Willdampia formosa*.

The subtitle to this book is 'Australia's first natural historian', and that is the focus — the plants and animals encountered by Dampier at Shark Bay, in the Archipelago named after him, and at Lagrange Bay. No-one could be better equipped than Alex George, a scrupulously careful taxonomist who has visited several of the sites and has sighted Dampier's specimens. He visited the most significant site, on Dirk Hartog Island, from a sailing ship, the STS *Leeuwin*, a stroke of good fortune that lends authenticity to the experience, and he studied the specimens, now housed in the herbarium at Oxford, in 1968 during a term as Australian Botanical Liaison Officer at the Royal Botanic Gardens, Kew, and reviewed previous work on them. This is therefore an authoritative account of the first surviving plants collected by Europeans in Australia and subjected to professional scrutiny. The illustrations in Dampier's work *A Voyage to New Holland* (1703) are the first published drawings of Australian flora and fauna.

So the present book is an obligatory addition to botanical and taxonomic libraries, but it should also serve to whet the appetite for more Dampier. He is, at least on the surface, a mass of contradictions that has led to diverse descriptions such as an 'English gentleman' (Giles Milton, in Beken, 1998), while the portrait by Thomas Murray in the National Portrait Gallery in London bears the title 'Captain William Dampier: Pirate and Hydrographer'. He was undoubtedly both, and he was also a pirate (or privateer) who collected plants. Further, he collected selectively, choosing those that he had not seen elsewhere (and in travelling three times round the world he saw a great deal). He pressed his specimens carefully and professionally: Alex George says that some of his specimens at Oxford are as well preserved as those collected recently.

Dampier visited the Galapagos where he and his crew 'refreshed ourselves very well with both Land and Sea-Turtles' which were 'extra-ordinarily large and fat, and so sweet that no Pullet eats more pleasantly'. He described star-fruit, the avocado, the sapodilla and many other tropical fruits from the Caribbean — and noted that when the Spaniards held Jamaica they established plantations of all these fruits, but when the island came into English possession, 'I never saw any improvement made by the English, who seem in that regard little curious'. This remark shows a degree of detachment rare in a time of rampant patriotic prejudice. Dampier, however, was curious about all he saw, with the same observant eye that Watkin Tench brought to Botany Bay a hundred years later.

Dampier kept copious notes, and treasured them, often under extremely difficult physical conditions. When the *Roebuck* came to grief at Ascension Island, he took them with him. When he was picked up and returned to Britain he was court-martialled on three counts, including the loss of his ship. He was found guilty of only one of the three charges, but nonetheless was fined three years' pay. To recover his fortune, he took to the pen, and thus joined a long succession of English travel writers, ranging from Sir John Mandeville (*Travels*, 1496) through to contemporaries of our day, like Eric Newby and Bruce Chatwin. Dampier is as good as any of them, sharp and direct in his records; and unlike any other travel writer that I have read, he hacked his way across the Isthmus of Panama, cutting a swathe through obstacles both physical and human. He reached the Pacific, sacked a few Spanish towns, commandeered a Spanish vessel, returned to the Caribbean, joined another band of privateers and sailed around Cape Horn and across the Pacific. This is the man who recognised the botanical riches of arid Shark Bay, collected solicitously, and preserved, against all odds, specimens that 300 years later still lie in a herbarium at Oxford. This equally meticulous monograph is a fitting memorial.

Introduction

The concept for this book, at first as an account of Dampier's Australian plants, emerged some years ago but remained dormant mainly because I could not see a way to obtain photographs from the localities where Dampier landed in 1699. Although I visited Dirk Hartog Island in 1972 I did not photograph all the species collected by him. An invitation to join a Maritime Heritage Voyage on STS *Leeuwin* in August–September 1998 gave me the opportunity to land on the island, as near as can be judged to the place where Dampier went ashore in August 1699. We also landed on Bernier Island which was visited by some of Dampier's crew. Although the weather during our visit to Dirk Hartog Island was rather cloudy with intermittent rain, my photographs turned out reasonably well, so I decided to proceed with the book. In January 1999 I visited Karrakatta Bay and Lagrange Bay to study the vegetation and photograph the sites where Dampier landed in 1688 and 1699 respectively. Several colleagues provided slides of East Lewis Island and Lagrange Bay and of the relevant plants there.

As I developed the concept, it became clear that it would be incomplete, as an account of Dampier the natural historian, without discussion of the animals that he described. I am extremely grateful to staff of the Western Australian Museum for their contribution in determining the modern names of Dampier's animals and supplying colour slides. John Huisman and Roberta Cowan, School of Biological Sciences, Murdoch University, determined Dampier's seaweed, assisted in the search for the specimen, and lent the colour slide reproduced here.

I also decided to include a short account of Dampier's earlier visit to New Holland, in 1688.

Acknowledgements

For discussions on Dampier's plants I thank Bruce Maslin, Paul Wilson, Nicholas Lander, Tim Willing, Kevin Kenneally, Gordon Graham, Keith Morris and Andrew Burbidge, of the Department of Conservation and Land Management, Western Australia; Roberta Cowan and John Huisman, School of Biological Sciences, Murdoch University, Perth; Helen Hewson, Gunning, New South Wales; Bob Chinnock and David Symon, State Herbarium of South Australia, Adelaide; Philip Short, Northern Territory Herbarium, Parks and Wildlife Commission of the Northern Territory, Darwin; Lyn Craven, Brendan Lepschi and Judy West, Australian National Herbarium, CSIRO, Canberra; Jim Ross, National Herbarium of Victoria, South Yarra, Melbourne.

Serena Marner, Fielding–Druce Herbarium, Oxford University, provided information on Dampier's plant specimens held there, arranged for the photograph of his specimen of seaweed, and assisted in obtaining various other information.

Alex Chapman, Australian Botanical Liaison Officer, Royal Botanic Gardens, Kew, searched (unfortunately without success) for the specimen on which Plukenet's account of *Acanthocarpus robustus* was based.

Paddy Berry, Clay Bryce, Terry Houston, Barry Hutchins, Ron Johnstone, Di Jones, Sue Morrison, Shirley Slack-Smith and Laurie Smith, all of the Western Australian Museum, Perth, were most helpful in identifying Dampier's animals from his drawings and written descriptions, providing advice on zoological nomenclature as well as photographs.

Gren Lucas, formerly Keeper, Royal Botanic Gardens, Kew, was most helpful in tracking down information on the memorials at East Coker, with assistance from the European Office of the Government of Western Australia in London and the Vicar of St Michael's Church, East Coker. He also assisted the search for information on the change from the Julian to the Gregorian calendar.

Pat Lowe and Jimmy Pike, of Broome, were great companions on my visit to Karrakatta Bay and Lagrange Bay in January 1999. John Dudu, of the Karajarri people at Bidyadanga, graciously guided us to Dampier's landing site at Lagrange Bay.

Greg Lowe, of the Perth Observatory, Bickley, assisted in ascertaining the date of the eclipse at Lagrange Bay in September 1699.

Slides were provided by John Huisman, Murdoch University; Ann and Wayne Storrie, Naturescapes, Perth; Chris Burton, Perth; Michael Morcombe, Armadale; Vivien Matson-Larkin, Osborne Park; Kevin Kenneally, Gordon Graham, Keith Morris and Andrew Burbidge, Department of Conservation and Land Management, Perth; Stephen van Leeuwen, Department of Conservation and Land Management, Karratha; Lochman Transparencies, Hamersley; and Brian Carter, One Arm Point.

Graeme Simpson scanned and copied, onto compact disc, pages from the first edition of Dampier's *Voyage to New Holland* while it was being prepared for rebinding by the Preservation Services Branch of the Library and Information Service of Western Australia.

In August–September 1998, the Leeuwin Ocean Adventure Association invited me to join a heritage voyage from Carnarvon to the Shark Bay islands and the Abrolhos Islands. Under Phillip Playford's guidance we landed at the site where Dampier is believed to have landed in August 1699. We also visited Bernier Island, where several of Dampier's crew landed, and then sailed south along the coast to the Abrolhos Islands. On a memorable, instructive voyage, Captain Peter Petroff, the crew and passengers of STS *Leeuwin* were enthusiastic participants in discovering the fascination of these historic parts of Australia.

John Maslin entered the project enthusiastically to design and draw the map showing Dampier's routes and landing places.

Roberta Cowan, Pat Lowe, Bruce Maslin, Phillip Playford and Paul Wilson offered constructive criticism of the manuscript.

As an Honorary Research Associate of the Western Australian Herbarium, I have appreciated access to the library and specimens housed there. Staff of the State Reference Library and the J.S. Battye Library of West Australian History, Perth, assisted my consultation of literature on William Dampier and made available copies of pages from Dampier's *Voyage to New Holland* (1703) for reproduction. Pages from Ray (1704) and Plukenet (1705) were photographed from copies held at the library of the Royal Botanic Gardens, Melbourne. The Bureau of Meteorology provided data on rainfall in 1998 for Steep Point, just south of Dirk Hartog Island (there is now no official recording station on the island). The Department of Land Administration provided data on place names that commemorate Dampier and the two ships in which he visited New Holland. Australia Post provided information on the postage stamps that commemorate Dampier. Details of the commemorative panels at the entrance to the Mitchell Library, State Library of New South Wales, Sydney, were provided by the Mitchell Librarian.

A slide of the portrait of Dampier was made available by the National Portrait Gallery, London, and a copy of an illustration of a ship similar to the *Roebuck* by the National Maritime Museum, Greenwich. The Museum also assisted with advice on the correct form of giving the names of British naval ships and the system of rating ships. The Hunt Institute for Botanical Documentation at the Carnegie Mellon University, Pittsburgh, provided copies of the portraits of Ray and Plukenet.

Alex George
School of Biological Sciences, Murdoch University
Perth

Notes on the text

In compiling a brief account of Dampier and his voyages I have drawn on his journals, several biographies, especially those by Lloyd (1966) and Gill (1997), and works such as Tuckfield (1955) and L.R. Marchant (1988).

Quotes from Dampier's journal of his visit in 1699 follow the first edition of *A Voyage to New Holland* (1703). Later editions and quotes that I have seen contain variations in spelling, capitalisation and punctuation.

Dates As was the practice in Britain at the time, Dampier used the Julian calendar. To assist readers to relate events in his life to the modern (Gregorian) calendar, I have converted all dates recorded by him by adding 10 days up to 28 February 1700, and 11 days thereafter. Where both dates are used, Dampier's (Julian) date appears in square brackets (see discussion pp. 149–150).

Place names generally are those currently in use, but 'New Holland' and several unofficial early names are used where relevant. Dampier himself rarely named places, 'Shark's Bay' and 'Rosemary Island' being the only two on the Western Australian coast. As explained below, the name Rosemary Island is now applied to an island different from the one that Dampier visited, the latter now being known as East Lewis Island.

Plant and animal names are given in the form set out in the *International Code of Botanical Nomenclature* (Greuter et al., 1994) and *International Code of Zoological Nomenclature* (Ride et al., 1985) respectively. In each, the name of the genus is followed by the name (epithet) for the species, then the author or authors, i.e. the person(s) who devised and published the species name. For the citation of authors the Codes differ in one point. Where organisms are still known under the genus in which they were first described, the author is cited without brackets. In the case of a plant species that has been transferred later to another genus, the original author is cited in brackets, followed outside the brackets by the author who made the transfer; inclusion of the date(s) is optional. For example, *Alyogyne pinoniana* (Gaudichaud) Fryxell was originally published in 1826 as *Hibiscus pinonianus* by Gaudichaud, then transferred to the genus *Alyogyne* by Fryxell in 1968. For animals, only the name of the original author is cited in brackets, with the date — the name of the transferring author is omitted. For example, the Green Turtle is now known as *Chelonia mydas* (Linnaeus, 1758) but was originally named by Linnaeus as *Testudo mydas*; the name of the author who transferred the species to *Chelonia* (in this case J.V.B. Bocage) and the date of transfer (1866) can be discovered only by consulting a work that gives synonymy.

The authors of plant names are commonly abbreviated, usually following a standard list (Brummitt and Powell, 1992), but here are given in full, as are those for animal names.

For flowering plants, ferns, fungi and most algae, modern nomenclature dates from 1 May 1753, the date of publication of *Species Plantarum* by Carl Linnaeus (Linné), who devised the binomial system of naming organisms — a standard name of two words, the genus and the species (Stearn, 1957). Prior to that, there was no accepted form, most organisms being given a short descriptive phrase that was usually several words long, often varying from author to author. This was the practice in Dampier's day. By international agreement, no plant name published before 1753 is now accepted (although many modern names are based on those used earlier).

For animals, the starting date of modern nomenclature is 1 January 1758.

When citing L.R. Marchant (1988) as a reference I have included the page number(s) since the book has no index. I also give his initials so as to distinguish between his work and the section by his brother N.G. Marchant in the same book.

Dampier's English

To the modern reader Dampier's writing is readily understandable. For the most part his use of words is similar to ours, and generally his spelling (in his published works) is the same. This is especially interesting in the scientific terminology. It appears, however, that the classical Latin word 'species' was not yet in general use in the modern scientific sense; Dampier generally uses 'sort' instead. Among the few words and phrases less familar now are to 'jog along' (in the sense of sailing gently), to 'clap on a wind' (to bring the ship's head closer to the wind), and 'knibs' (branchlets of trees). A quote from Dampier is given as an example of this usage of 'jog' in *The Oxford English Dictionary*. Different spellings include 'smoak' for smoke. He used capitals for many nouns, and commonly omitted the 'e' from the past tense ending '–ed', e.g. engag'd, steer'd, sail'd; he also used the contemporary past tense form 'mixt' etc., 'tho' instead of though, and 'mould' for soil. There is considerable inconsistency in spelling, punctuation (especially use of commas, semicolons, apostrophes and hyphens) and capitalisation.

For place names and natural history objects, Dampier wrote, in the preface to his *New Voyage* of 1697, that 'I have not been curious [i.e. particular] as to the spelling of the Names of Places, Plants, Fruits, Animals, &c. which in any of these remoter parts are given at the pleasure of Travellers, and vary according to their different Humours.' Italic typeface is generally used in his journals for the names of countries.

Chronology of William Dampier's life

1651	Baptised at East Coker, Somerset, England (5 September)
1658	Father died
1665	Mother died
1669	Apprenticed to shipmaster in Weymouth, sailing to France, Newfoundland and Java
1672	Enlisted in the Royal Navy; saw service in the battle of Texel against the Dutch (August 1673)
1674	Sailed for Jamaica to work for William Whaley, manager of a plantation
1675	Joined privateers in the Caribbean
1678	Returned to England; married Judith
1679	Sailed to Jamaica and joined a group of privateers
1680–81	With privateers crossed the Isthmus of Panama; sacked towns on the Pacific coast; captured a ship and sailed to the Juan Fernandez Islands, then returned to Darien and crossed back to the Caribbean coast at La Sounds Key
1682	Lived for more than a year on a tobacco plantation in Virginia
1683–84	Joined John Cook in the *Revenge* and sailed across the Atlantic to Sierra Leone where they seized a Danish ship which they renamed the *Batchelor's Delight*; rounded Cape Horn and sailed up the Pacific coast of South America and spent many months attacking towns and ships
1685	Transferred to the *Cygnet* under Charles Swan
1686	Sailed across the Pacific from Mexico to Guam; Swan replaced as captain by John Reed (Read)
1686–87	Cruised the China Sea, visited Canton, Thailand and various islands
1687	Sailed south past Timor

1688	Reached north-western New Holland (January) and landed near Swan Point, east of Cape Leveque
1688	Sailed west into the Indian Ocean, past Christmas Island, to the Nicobar Islands where he was put ashore (May), then sailed in an open canoe to Achin (Sumatra); joined an East Indiaman and sailed to Tonquin (Vietnam), then made his way back to Achin (March 1689), joined ships to Malacca and Madras; briefly in charge of a fort at Bencoolen for the East India Company; acquired an Indonesian slave, Jeoly
1690	Left for England in the *Defence* under Captain Heath, calling at Cape Town and St Helena; reached the Downs, off Deal (26 September 1691)
1697	Published *A New Voyage Round the World*
1698	Submitted proposal to the British Admiralty for a voyage to the East Indies and New Holland
1699	Published *A Supplement to the Voyage Round the World* and *A Discourse of Trade-winds, etc.*
1699	Sailed from the Downs in the *Roebuck* (24 January); at Bahia, Brazil (March–April); approached west coast of New Holland (August); anchored in Shark Bay and landed on Dirk Hartog Island (17 August); landed on East Lewis Island, Dampier Archipelago (1 September); landed at Lagrange Bay (9–15 September); at Timor (October–November)
1700	Sailing around New Guinea, New Ireland, then headed home via Cape Town
1701	*Roebuck* foundered off Ascension Island, South Atlantic (6 March)
1701	Picked up by British ships (14 April); arrived in England (August 1701)
1702	Court-martialled for his treatment of Fisher and Norwood, and for the loss of the *Roebuck*; cleared on last two charges, fined on first
1703	Published *A New Voyage to New Holland &c in the Year 1699*
1703	Left England in command of the *St George* for a privateering voyage to the Pacific; at Kinsale, Ireland, teamed up with the

Cinque Ports, Captain Charles Pickering; then to Cape Verde Islands, Brazil, Juan Fernandez; took several ships but missed the prize of a 'Manila ship' (December 1704); sacked the Mexican town of Puna, then captured a Spanish ship for the voyage home across the Pacific — but no details remain of this part of his adventures

1707   Arrived back in England

1708   Left on his final voyage (September), as navigator under Woodes Rogers in the *Duke* and the *Dutchess* (Captain Stephen Courtney), again privateering — via Grande, South America, Falkland Islands, Cape Horn, Juan Fernadez (picking up Alexander Selkirk), taking several Spanish ships and a French one; sacked Guayaquil (April 1709)

1709   *Continuation of a New Voyage to New Holland &c in the Year 1699* (the later part of the voyage of 1699–1701) published in London

1710   Crossed the Pacific (January), arriving at Guam (11 March), then via The Philippines, Celebes, Batavia, Cape Town, St Helena, Ascension, around the north of Scotland to Amsterdam (24 July 1711); returned to London in September 1711

1715   Died at the Old Jewry, London, England (March; will proven on 3 April)

William Dampier —
natural historian, author,
adventurer, privateer

IN AUGUST AND SEPTEMBER 1699, William Dampier became the first Englishman to gather plant specimens in Australia, at that time known as New Holland. During a voyage of exploration from England to the south-western Pacific Ocean and back, he landed at three sites on the north-west coast of what is now Western Australia. Besides gathering plants he also described the landscape and soils and recorded observations on many marine and land animals.

It is evident from his published work that Dampier was well versed in natural history, indeed that it was a major interest in his extensive travels around the world. He wrote that 'The further we went the more knowledge and experience I should get ... which was the main thing I regarded'. His journals contain many descriptions and observations of plants and animals that reflect a broad knowledge of natural history acquired from the countries he visited. He knew the names of many plants, birds, marine and land animals; he described them in scientific terms (many of which are still used); and he compared or contrasted his discoveries with those seen elsewhere. One of his crew drew animals and plants, in a style as realistic as any being drawn at that period — as will be seen below, most are readily recognisable even without the specimens.

On his return to England he did not simply lay aside his plant collections and drawings as curiosities, but handed them to a member of the Royal Society, Thomas Woodward, who in turn passed them to the leading English botanists John Ray and Leonard Plukenet for study. Dampier included an English translation of Ray's account (published in Latin in 1704) in his book on the voyage (1703). For the animals he seems to have been content to rely on his own observations; at least there is no acknowledgement of others in his book except for mention of the works *Ichthyographia* (1685) and *Historia Piscium* (1686) by Francis Willughby (1635–1672) and one by Willem Piso (1611–1678), probably his *De Indiae* etc. of 1658.

Dampier's journal provided the first broad account of the Australian environment, with notes on the landscape, soils, vegetation, tides, the sea floor, winds and weather. Among his surviving specimens are 23 species of Australian flowering plants and a seaweed. Two more plants can be recognised from figures in the work of Leonard Plukenet who described some of the specimens. From Dampier's journal we can recognise a further six species of plants, one phytoplankton, 17 birds, 14 fishes, three marine mammals, two or three terrestrial mammals including one or two marsupials, one land reptile, three marine reptiles (including turtles), three molluscs (including two oysters), one cephalopod and one insect. Other general comments refer to unidentifiable seashells and birds and another marine alga. Indeed, Dampier might be called the 'Father of Australian natural history'. Had he been able to talk to the Aborigines he would doubtless have become fascinated by their intimate association with the environment that provided all their daily needs.

Prior to Dampier's visit, several Dutch voyagers had made observations on the natural history of the western coastline of New Holland. Following the wreck of the *Batavia* on the Abrolhos Islands in June 1629, Francisco Pelsaert recorded the Tammar Wallaby (*Macropus eugenii*) and birds on the Wallabi Islands. In January 1697, Willem de Vlamingh explored Rottnest Island and the Swan River and described black swans (*Cygnus atratus*), quokkas (*Setonix brachyurus*), Rottnest Island cypress (*Callitris preissii*) and tea-tree (*Melaleuca lanceolata*), trees dripping gum (either *Acacia* or *Eucalyptus*) and zamia fruit (*Macrozamia riedlei*) (Playford, 1998). During landings made as they sailed northwards, Vlamingh's crew twice mentioned seeing the tracks of 'tigers', presumably the Dingo (*Canis lupus dingo*). It is possible, but as yet has not been demonstrated conclusively, that specimens of *Acacia truncata* and *Synaphea spinulosa*, the first Australian plants named (in 1768) under the modern Linnaean system of plant nomenclature, were collected during Vlamingh's visit. If so, they are the first gathered by Europeans in Australia, but until such proof is forthcoming, Dampier's specimens remain the earliest authenticated collection from this continent (George, 1971; Maslin, 1978). Vlamingh did take back timber from the cypress and tea-tree, oil distilled from the wood, gum samples (possibly from Marri, *Eucalyptus calophylla*) and seeds. He placed a post hewn from a cypress trunk beside that of Dirk Hartog on Dirk Hartog Island, but there is now no trace of the other collections (Nelson, 1994).

Dampier's early decades

There are few details of Dampier's early years. The third child of George and Anne (or Ann) Dampier, who were tenant farmers, William Dampier was born in the village of East Coker, Somerset, England, being baptised on 15 September 1651. This was the period of Oliver Cromwell's Republic. His father died when he was seven and his mother when he was 14, but guardians ensured that he received a good education, including attendance at a 'Latin school' (one that included Latin in its syllabus).

In 1669 he went to sea in a Weymouth trader. On various voyages and ships he visited France, Newfoundland and Java. He then enlisted on the *Royal Prince* (commanded by Sir Edward Spragge) which participated in two battles with the Dutch navy, the second being the battle of Texel in August 1673. In 1674 he sailed to Jamaica where he worked on a sugar plantation, then sailed on various ships around the Caribbean. Soon he turned to the timber trade, in particular harvesting campeachy wood

(*Haematoxylum campechianum*), the dark heartwood of which was used in the production of dye, ink and furniture. Cut illegally from Spanish territory in Central America, campeachy wood was exported very profitably to Britain. Dampier then became involved in privateering against Spanish ships, and returned to England in August 1678. There he married, but in the spring of 1679 he was again at sea around the West Indies and the Spanish Main. On his early voyages, including that of 1699–1701, he kept a journal which he stored in lengths of bamboo sealed with wax.

Until 1686 he was again engaged in privateering in various ships against the Spanish. Strictly speaking it is probably incorrect to label Dampier a 'buccaneer', a term used originally for people who smoked and dried meat, and later applied to sailors who practised piracy (Lloyd, 1966; L.R. Marchant, 1988, pp. 42–49). Privateering was an acceptable, even respected, occupation in the eyes of the British, since it was carried out against enemy nations and their territories. A privateer operated under a licence and might be financed by businessmen. In 1680 Dampier participated in a privateering expedition across the Isthmus of Panama, raiding Spanish towns on the Pacific coast. By 1682 he was in Virginia where he stayed for 13 months, but we do not know how he was occupied during this period.

In August 1683 he joined the ship *Revenge* under Captain John Cook, sailing to Africa, where they captured a Danish slave ship, renamed her the *Batchelor's Delight* (after Alderman John Batchelor of Bristol, Master of the Society of Merchant Venturers in England) and sailed in her around Cape Horn to the Pacific coast of central America. For a time they joined a fleet of ten ships that plundered Spanish vessels. In 1685, Dampier transferred to the *Cygnet*, captained by Charles Swan, and in 1686 they sailed across the Pacific to Guam, a distance of over 11 000 kilometres which they covered in 51 days. They continued to Mindanao, where Swan was replaced as captain by John Reed (also spelt Read). During the next 18 months they visited islands in that region as well as Thailand and China. We do not know what rank Dampier held on the *Cygnet*.

✳

First visit to New Holland

Late in 1687, sailing the *Cygnet* southwards from the Celebes, they passed the western end of Timor and on 14 January 1688 made landfall in New Holland, possibly near the Lacepede Islands in 16°50′S latitude, becoming the first British vessel to reach the mainland coast of Australia. They then turned north-east and rounded Swan Point at the northern tip of what is now the Dampier Peninsula. Sailing into King Sound they first anchored, on 15 or 16 January, near Salural Island (L.R. Marchant, 1988, pp. 70, 109). They landed on one or more of the islands in this vicinity and made contact with Aborigines, who Dampier described in some detail. About a week later (according to Dampier, three weeks according to L.R. Marchant, 1988, p. 70) 'we hauled our Ship into a small sandy Cove, at Spring-tide'. L.R. Marchant (pp. 112–121) determined that this was in a small cove on the north side of Karrakatta Bay, just south-west of Swan Point. Here, over the next few weeks, they careened the ship and repaired the sails. According to Dampier's own book, they remained there until 22 March, though a manuscript in the British Library gives the date as 22 February (L.R. Marchant, 1988, p. 64). Dampier spent considerable time ashore and recorded details of the natural history.

Some confusion arose later over the bay where they careened the *Cygnet*, due largely to the use of the name Cygnet Bay which some writers have assumed was the site of the 1688 landing (L.R. Marchant, 1988, p. 120). In August 1821, Phillip Parker King gave the name to the whole large bay east of Swan Point, but in 1838 John Lort Stokes renamed it King Sound and gave the name Cygnet Bay to an embayment on the west side of the Sound well south of the area visited by the *Cygnet*.

In his published account of the voyage (1697), Dampier wrote:

The Land is of a dry sandy Soil, destitute of Water, except you make Wells; yet producing divers sorts of Trees; but the Woods are not thick, nor the Trees very big. Most of the Trees that we saw are Dragon-trees as we supposed; and these too are the largest trees of any there. They are about the bigness of our large Apple-trees, and about the same heighth: and the Rind is blackish, and somewhat rough. The Leaves are of a dark colour; the Gum distils out of the knots or cracks that are in the Bodies of the Trees. We compared it with some Gum Dragon, or Dragons Blood, that was aboard; and it was of the same colour and taste. The other sorts of Trees were not known by any of us. There was pretty long Grass growing under the Trees, but it was very thin. We saw no Trees that bore Fruit or Berries.

We saw no sort of Animal, nor any track of Beast, but once; and that seemed to be the tread of a Beast as big as a great Mastiff-Dog. Here are a few small Land-birds, but none bigger than a Blackbird; and but few Sea-fowls. Neither is the sea very plentifully stored with Fish, unless you reckon the Manatee and Turtle as such. Of these Creatures there is plenty, but they are extraordinary shy; though the Inhabitants cannot trouble them much, having neither Boats nor Iron.

The beach where the *Cygnet* is thought to have been careened is of white sand, with rugged sandstone outcrops at each end. Towards Swan Point the dunes are openly vegetated with clumps of *Pandanus*, a few *Melaleuca* and other small trees. There are large expanses of sand where the crew could have erected their tents. Low-lying areas carry low grass (mainly *Sporobolus*). West of the careening site the land rises slightly and becomes more densely covered with a low woodland, mainly of wattle, but within a few kilometres other trees occur, including the bloodwood *Eucalyptus dampieri*, appropriately so named by Denis Carr and Maisie Carr in 1987. This vegetation is savannah typical of the Dampier Peninsula (Beard, 1979; Kenneally et al., 1996). The bloodwoods are the trees that exude the red gum that reminded Dampier of dragon's blood — the gum released by the Dragon Tree, *Dracaena draco* (Linnaeus) Linnaeus, of the Madeira, Canary and Cape Verde Islands (Marrero et al., 1998). Several authors, e.g. Beaglehole (1962), have assumed that it was also the *Dracaena* that Dampier saw here, while others, e.g. L.R. Marchant (1988, p. 115), and N.G. Marchant (1988, p. 194), considered that it was a screw pine (*Pandanus*). *Dracaena* does not occur in Australia, and *Pandanus*, although it resembles *Dracaena* in habit and occurs at the landing site, does not exude gum. The description of the leaves as dark-coloured and the bark as having knots or cracks fits bloodwoods rather than *Pandanus*.

Mangroves occur in extensive bands close to the shore in Karrakatta Bay. If their distribution is similar to that of 1688, then the 'third cove' from the east, as determined by L.R. Marchant (1988, pp. 114–116), is the only one that allows sufficient room to bring a ship ashore.

The animal leaving footprints like a mastiff would have been the dingo (*Canis lupus dingo*). Manatee is the Caribbean name for a sea cow (described in detail by Dampier elsewhere in this journal), and in north-western Australia would refer to the Dugong (*Dugong dugon*). The turtle was probably the Green Turtle (*Chelonia mydas*).

After leaving New Holland, Reed and his crew sailed the *Cygnet* to the Nicobar Islands where Dampier left the ship. Following further voyaging in the region he returned to England in the British ship *Defence*, arriving on 26 September 1691. Details of his activities for the next six years are few, but he wrote an account of his travels that was published in 1697 as *A New Voyage Round the World*. Besides the narrative, he included information on sailing in the tropics, natural history and observations on peoples of many lands. The book became popular, going through five editions by 1703, and brought Dampier fame as an acknowledged expert in these matters. It was translated into Dutch (1698), French (1698) and German (1702). His detailed account of sailing in the tropics was published in 1699 as *A Discourse of Trade-winds, Breezes, Storms, Seasons of the Year*, etc.

✳

The *Roebuck* voyage

In 1698 Dampier requested of the British Admiralty a ship to explore New Holland and seek commercial prospects. He was given the *Roebuck*, a 290-ton, three-masted, square-rigged barque with a length of 96 feet (about 30 metres) and a beam of 25 feet (about 8 metres), built at Wapping on the River Thames, and fitted out for the voyage at Deptford. She was a sixth-rate ship with a capacity of 70 crew and 26 guns, but on this voyage she carried 50 crew and 12 guns (sixth-rate ships carried fewer than 32 guns).

They departed England on 24 January 1699. After calling at Bahia in Brazil (where the First Lieutenant, George Fisher, was put ashore after violent arguments with Dampier), they sailed directly for New Holland, bypassing Cape Town. This was still the period when longitude could not be calculated accurately, but by early August 1699 Dampier reckoned that he was close to the Abrolhos Islands, off the lower-central west coast of Australia. They saw various seaweeds and other marine objects floating on the sea, as well as 'Abundance of Scuttle-bones'. At first Dampier believed he was to the south of the Abrolhos and turned southwards to avoid them, then decided they were to the south and turned to the north, then a further reach south, and then north again, moving closer to the coast, which was first seen at 9 in the morning of 10 August.

For several days Dampier followed the Zuytdorp Cliffs before seeing South Passage, a narrow strait between Dirk Hartog Island and Steep Point, the westernmost point of the Australian mainland. Wisely deciding against attempting to enter here, he stood out to sea and continued north. The weather was a typical showery winter's day in south-western Australia: they experienced strong westerly winds that 'blow very fierce while the Squals of Rain were over our Heads; but as soon as they were gone the Wind was by much abated, the stress of the Storm being over'. On 16 August 1699 they entered Shark Bay between Cape Inscription (at the north end of Dirk Hartog Island) and Dorre Island. Skirting a large shoal (Levillain Shoal), Dampier anchored off what is now called Dampier Landing (near Sammy Well), north of Cape Withnell and about 5 kilometres south-east of Cape Inscription.

They remained four days at this anchorage. Dampier went ashore on Dirk Hartog Island on the morning of 17 August and probably on other days. While the crew cut firewood and searched (unsuccessfully) for water, he explored some way inland (the island at that point is about 7 kilometres across). He described it thus:

Tis all a steep Shore against the open Sea: but in this Bay or Sound we were now in, the Land is low by the Sea-side, rising gradually in within the Land. The Mould is Sand by the Sea-side, producing a large sort of Sampier, which bears a white Flower. Farther in, the Mould is reddish, a sort of Sand producing some Grass, Plants, and Shrubs. The Grass grows in great Tufts, as big as a Bushel, here and there a Tuft: being intermix'd with much Heath, much of the kind we have growing on our Commons in *England*. Of Trees or Shrubs here are divers sorts; but none above ten Foot high: Their Bodies about 3 Foot about, and 5 or 6 Foot high before you come to the Branches, which are bushy and compos'd of small Twigs there spreading abroad, tho' thick set, and full of Leaves; which were mostly long and narrow. The Colour of the Leaves was on one Side whitish, and on the other Green; and the Bark of the Trees was generally of the same Colour with the Leaves, of a pale green. Some of these Trees were sweet-scented, and reddish within the Bark, like Sassafras, but redder. Most of the Trees and Shrubs had at this Time either Blossoms or Berries on them. The Blossoms of the different sort of Trees were of several Colours, as Red, White, Yellow, &c., but mostly Blue: and these generally smelt very sweet and fragrant, as did some also of the rest. There were also beside some Plants, Herbs, and tall Flowers, some very small Flowers, growing on the Ground, that were sweet and beautiful, and for the most part unlike any I had seen elsewhere.

When we landed from STS *Leeuwin* on 27 August 1998, we found the area in what must have been a very similar state to that seen by Dampier.

Immediately above the white sandy beach were large shrubs of the Nitre Bush (*Nitraria billardierei*), in full flower, resembling the European samphire ('sampier'), *Crithmum maritimum*. Behind were high sand dunes, and quite quickly we reached the more stabilised pale red sand and low but dense vegetation where Dampier collected his specimens. Only a rough vehicle track disturbed a scene that otherwise must have looked much as it did to Dampier and his men. Here we found species collected by Dampier — *Diplolaena, Acacia, Dampiera, Hannafordia, Conostylis,* etc. *Beaufortia* and *Thryptomene* were common. Between the shrubs were his grasses 'in great Tufts', *Spinifex longifolius* on the coastal dunes, *Triodia danthonioides* inland, and perhaps he walked far enough to see another spinifex, *Triodia plurinervata*. In the open spaces between were small ephemeral herbs, the brilliant *Calandrinia* and *Lotus*. And throughout were his blue flowers — the *Dampiera, Solanum* and *Brachycome* that are among his specimens, and others that he must have seen, may have collected and later lost or discarded — *Halgania, Scaevola, Alyogyne* and another *Brachycome*. What is more, the vegetation was in excellent condition after the winter rains. Even the ephemerals were of similar size to those in Dampier's collection, so clearly he too was there in a 'good' season. The average annual rainfall (1893–1948) for Dirk Hartog Island homestead (towards the southern end of the island) is just over 300 mm but quite variable, ranging from 120 to 680 mm, falling mainly in winter. In 1998, Steep Point, just south of the island, received 305 mm of rain from May to August.

The main tree that Dampier described appears to be the Native Willow, *Pittosporum phylliraeoides*, which is scattered through the heath and rises above it. Another possibility is *Alectryon* (formerly *Hetero-dendrum*) *oleifolius*, recorded from the island but not observed near Dampier's landing place. Plants with berry-like fruit at this season include *Myoporum, Pimelea microcephala, Solanum* and *Pittosporum*. *Nitraria* also has a berry-like fruit but is in flower in August. The small ground herbs include *Calandrinia, Brachycome* and other small daisies, and another grass collected by Dampier, *Paractaenum*. It is likely that he collected the *Ptilotus* that was illustrated by Plukenet but is no longer among his specimens. As he did so often, Dampier compared the plants he saw with those he knew, in this instance writing that they were 'for the most part unlike any I had seen elswhere'. Later research has confirmed the truth of this observation: many of the genera and all the species that he collected are endemic in Australia.

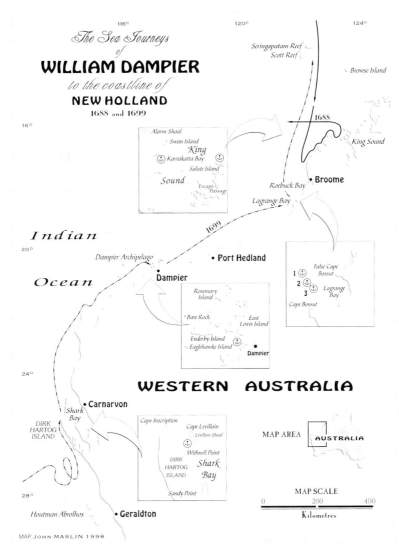

Map of Western Australia showing the probable routes of the *Cygnet* in 1688 and the *Roebuck* in 1699.

Drawn by John Maslin, East Fremantle

On 21 August they weighed anchor and sailed farther into Shark Bay, first to the south, then eastwards (anchoring near the middle of the Bay, north of Peron Peninsula), then north-westwards until they anchored to the east of the north end of Dorre Island on 22 August. On 23 August, while the *Roebuck* was being 'scrubbed', Dampier sent some men ashore on the 'most Northerly of the 2 Islands' (Bernier), and they reported 'that the Isle produces nothing but a sort of green, short, hard, prickly Grass, affording neither Wood nor fresh Water; and that a Sea broak between the two Islands, a Sign that the Water was shallow. They saw a large Turtle, and many Skates and Thornbacks, but caught none'. The prickly grass is the spinifex *Triodia plurinervata* which is more common on Bernier than on Dirk Hartog Island. When we landed on Bernier Island, I found *Trachymene elachocarpa* to be common, whereas I did not see it near Dampier Landing on Dirk Hartog Island (although I have seen it farther south). It is thus possible that the specimen of this species among Dampier's plants at Oxford University was gathered by one of his crew. The turtle was the Green Turtle (*Chelonia mydas*), the Skate was probably the Smooth Stingray (*Dasyatis brevicaudata*) and the Thornback may have been the Thorny Ray (*Urogymnus asperrimus*).

Dampier appears not to have seen the posts atop the cliff at Cape Inscription where Dirk Hartog in 1616 and Wilhelm de Vlamingh in 1697 left pewter plates with details of their visits.

After sailing between Dirk Hartog and Dorre Islands on 24 August, they headed north, making little progress the first day due to headwinds, but then with favourable winds they 'jogg'd along' and on 28 August apparently rounded North West Cape where, during the night of 28–29th, they were distressed by the sound of much blowing and performing of Humpback Whales — the splashing of water sounded like sea breaking on rocks.

Two days later saw them threading a careful passage through the Dampier Archipelago, anchoring off Enderby Island on 31 August. On 1 September, while anchored off East Lewis Island, Dampier landed and later wrote:

There grow here 2 or 3 sorts of Shrubs, one just like Rosemary; and therefore I call'd this *Rosemary* Island. It grew in great plenty here, but had no smell. Some of the other Shrubs had blue and yellow Flowers; and we found 2 sorts of Grain like Beans: The one grew on Bushes; the other on a sort of a creeping Vine that runs along the Ground, having very thick broad Leaves, and the Blossom like a Bean Blossom, but much larger, and of a deep red Colour, looking very beautiful ... The Stones were all of a rusty Colour, and Ponderous.

Due to an error made by the French navigator Louis de Freycinet (who sailed on the Baudin voyage of 1800–04), Dampier's 'Rosemary Island' was reckoned to be one of the outer islands of the Dampier Archipelago and this mistake was followed by later cartographers. Modern research has shown that Dampier's island is almost certainly East Lewis Island (Tuckfield, 1955; L.R. Marchant, 1997, pp. 138–142). This part of the Archipelago has natural heaps of dark reddish-brown boulders of Gidley Granophyre, an igneous intrusive rock thought to be about 3000 million years old. The 'Rosemary' is a species of *Olearia*, currently known as *Eurybia dampieri* but awaiting formal publication in *Olearia*. The grain that grew on bushes was almost certainly the bird-flower *Crotalaria cunninghamii*, which is common on coastal dunes of north-western Australia and farther inland and has greenish-yellow flowers. Dampier confused two species in his descripion of the vine that 'runs along the Ground'. The scarlet and black flowers clearly belong to the Sturt Pea, *Willdampia*, but the 'very thick broad leaves' fit not this species but either *Canavalia rosea* or *Ipomoea pes-caprae*, both beach plants common on tropical coasts. In contrast, Sturt Pea has small, soft leaflets. *Canavalia* has medium-sized pink pea flowers, and *Ipomoea* large tubular pink ones. Possibly all three were growing together and Dampier did not determine which flowers belonged to which leaves. The blue flower here was probably *Trichodesma zeylanicum*, again a common tropical plant.

On 3 September they sailed eastwards with a very strong sea breeze, moderating after noon, and dropping completely during the night when they caught 'a good Store of Fish'. For the next five days they 'coasted along the shore' and out to sea, before approaching the coast again at Lagrange Bay and anchoring on 9 September. Later writers considered that this last anchorage on the Australian coast was in the present-day Roebuck Bay (where Broome stands) or even further north (e.g. Yarrow, 1980), but Tuckfield (1955) demonstrated that it must have been in Lagrange Bay — confirmed by L.R. Marchant (1988, pp. 142–146). They remained there for about six days, twice moving the ship a little closer inshore. They spent considerable time seeking water but found only a brackish supply by digging. Here was their only encounter with the Aborigines on this voyage, but they were unsuccessful in their attempts to communicate with them. In describing the land, Dampier wrote:

When we came on the top of the Hill where they [the Aborigines] first stood, we saw a plain Savannah, about half a mile from us, farther in from the Sea. There were several Things like Hay-cocks, standing in the Savannah; which at a distance we thought were Houses, looking just like the *Hottentot*'s Houses at the *Cape of G. Hope*: but we found them to be so many Rocks ...

The Land hereabouts was much like the part of *New Holland* that I formerly described [Vol. I, p. 463] 'tis low, but seemingly barricado'd with a long Chain of Sand-hills to the Sea, that lets nothing be seen of what is farther within Land. At high Water the Tides rising so high as they do, the Coast shews very low: but when 'tis low Water it seems to be of an indifferent heighth. At low Water-Mark the Shore is all Rocky, so that then there is no Landing with a Boat; but at high Water a Boat may come in over those Rocks to the Sandy Bay, which runs all along this Coast. The Land by the Sea for about 5 or 600 yards is a dry Sandy Soil, bearing only Shrubs and Bushes of divers sorts. Some of these had them at this time of the year, yellow Flowers or Blossoms, some blue, and some white; most of them of a very fragrant Smell. Some had Fruit like Peasecods; in each of which there were just ten small Peas: I opened many of them, and found no more nor less. There are also here some of that sort of Bean which I saw at *Rosemary*-Island: and another sort of small, red, hard Pulse, growing in Cods also, with little black Eyes like Beans. I know not their Names, but have seen them used often in the *East-Indies* for weighing Gold; and they make the same use of them at *Guinea*, as I have heard, where the Women also make Bracelets with them to wear about their Arms. These grow on Bushes: but here are also a Fruit like Beans growing on a creeping sort of Shrub-like Vine. There was great plenty of all these sorts of Cod-fruit growing on the Sand-hills by the Sea-side, some of them green, some ripe, and some fallen on the Ground: but I could not perceive that any of them had been gathered by the Natives; and might not probably be wholesome Food.

The land farther in, that is lower than what borders on the Sea, was, so much as we saw of it, very plain and even; partly Savannahs, and partly Woodland. The Savannahs bear a sort of thin, course Grass. The Mould is also a courser Sand than that by the Sea-side, and in some places 'tis Clay. Here are a great many Rocks in the large Savannah we were in, which are 5 or 6 Foot high, and round at the top like a Hay-cock, very remarkable; some red, and some white. The Woodland lies farther in still; where there are divers sorts of small Trees, scarce any three Foot in circumference; their Bodies 12 or 14 Foot high, with a Head of small Knibs or Boughs. By the sides of the Creeks, especially nigh the Sea, there grow a few small black Mangrove-Trees.

Here Dampier has given a good description of the coastal landforms, soils and vegetation, from the dunes immediately above the beach to the plains inland, some open, some clothed in woodland. He erred, however, in thinking that the structures like 'Hay-cocks' were rocks. They are the termite mounds so common in northern Australia, built by a number of species and commonly also occupied by other fauna. They vary in shape and colour according to the species of termite and the local soil respectively. Those at Lagrange Bay are built by species of *Nasutitermes*, the grey ones on the clay soil that Dampier mentioned and the red ones on red loam. The bean seen also at East Lewis (Dampier's 'Rosemary') Island may be *Crotalaria cunninghamii*, which is very common on the dunes at Lagrange Bay, and the 'Fruit like Beans' on a creeping vine is *Canavalia rosea* (see above). The plant with red seeds having 'little black Eyes like Beans' is *Abrus precatorius*; this is not a bush as described by Dampier but scrambles over shrubs and sheds its leaves as the pods ripen, hence he apparently thought that the pods were produced by the shrubs. This is a widepread tropical plant and was possibly brought to Australia by ancestors of the Aborigines. He was correct in deducing that the Aborigines do not eat any of these. The seeds of *Abrus* are highly toxic, and those of both *Crotalaria* and *Canavalia* contain potentially toxic alkaloids, although with appropriate treatment they can be made edible (Everist, 1974). In this area, the trees of the savannah and woodland include various species of *Acacia*, *Eucalyptus*, *Bauhinia*, *Terminalia*, *Santalum* and *Melaleuca*. The most common mangrove there is *Avicennia marina*; other genera are *Aegialitis*, *Bruguiera*, *Camptostemon*, *Osbornia* and *Rhizophora* (Semeniuk et al., 1978).

At Lagrange Bay they saw an eclipse of the moon. Dampier's account mentions that 'the Horizon was very hazy, so that we could not see the Moon till she had been half an hour above the Horizon: and at two hours, 22 min. after Sun-set, by the reckoning of our Glasses, the Eclipse was quite gone'. The Master of the *Roebuck*, Jacob Hughes, wrote: 'last night observed the Eclipse of the Moon att his first rising there was ⅔ of his body darkened, I did not any ways perceive it to Encrease, at ½ past 8 it was over'. Modern calculations confirm that this was a partial eclipse and occurred on 9 September 1699, their first evening at Lagrange Bay, as described by Hughes. It is interesting that Dampier referred to the moon as female and Hughes as male.

After leaving Lagrange Bay on about 15 September they sailed north, passing an island (probably Browse Island), and on to Timor. They spent October and November there, then for some months explored eastwards around the northern coast of New Guinea and islands to the east. Although Dampier's plan had been to then sail south to find the east coast of New Holland, he decided, because of the poor state of the *Roebuck* and uncertainty over currents and coral reefs, that it was prudent to turn homewards. After calling at Batavia they reached Ascension Island in the southern Atlantic Ocean on 3 March 1701, where the ship developed a leak that could not be repaired. On 6 March the crew took essential items ashore and the next day removed the sails (for use as tents) and left the ship to sink. Dampier saved his journals and plant specimens. The crew lived mainly on turtles and goats, with water from a spring now named after Dampier. On 14 April a fleet of four British ships anchored in the bay and took them aboard, leaving the island on 19 April. Dampier sailed first on the *Anglesey*, then transferred to the East Indiaman *Canterbury*, arriving back in England in August 1701.

In 1702, Dampier was court-martialled on three counts: his treatment of Lieutenant Fisher, the circumstances of the death of boatswain Norwood, and the loss of his ship. He was cleared on the last two charges but found guilty on the first and fined three years' pay. Although this left him almost destitute, the publication of the first part of his *A Voyage to New Holland* in 1703 brought acclaim and acceptance in society again.

Later years

Dampier made two further voyages around the world but kept no journal on either, hence some detail is missing from the accounts of them. In 1703 he left as captain of the *St George* on a privateering voyage that took him into the Pacific Ocean via Cape Horn, visiting the Juan Fernandez Islands and spending about two years plundering ships, as well as towns on the southern and central American coasts. In the Gulf of Panama he captured a Spanish ship and transferred to it, leaving the now-rotten *St George* to sink. He then crossed the Pacific to Batavia and arrived home late in 1707. The voyage was plagued with dissension between Dampier and his crew.

His final voyage was from 1708 to 1711, as pilot and advisor on the *Duke* under Captain Woodes Rogers, accompanied by the *Dutchess* under the command of Stephen Courtney. Again they rounded Cape Horn, called at Juan Fernandez Island and operated as privateers along the Pacific American coast (including the prize of a Manila galleon). The voyage (with two captured ships) across the Pacific to Guam this time took 69 days. Continuing via the Philippines, Celebes and Batavia, they arrived in England in September 1711, on the final leg across the North Sea escorted by three ships of the Royal Navy! Division of the booty (valued at almost £150 000) among the owners of the ships, 'shareholders' in the venture and the crew took several years and was subject to some litigation. Dampier had not received all his due by the time he died.

Dampier lived out his years in London, in Coleman Street near the Old Jewry in the Parish of St Stephen. The date of his death is unrecorded, but his will was proven on 3 April [Julian 23 March] 1715; he was 63 years old. His place of burial is unknown.

Dampier the natural historian

Most authors have commented on Dampier's scientific records and their influence. He was clearly intrigued by natural science, far beyond the interest of the average adventurer or sailor who at most sought only useful plants and animals (those providing food, medicine or economic products). His observations show a mind interested in their form, distribution and behaviour. He observed all manner of plants from trees and shrubs to tiny herbs, seaweed and moss. He noted marine life, birds and land animals including reptiles. Besides attempting to identify them, he related plants and animals to those he had seen in different countries, a forerunner of modern systematic and biogeographical studies. In all, he gave an intriguing overview of the natural history of the coast of north-western Australia. Modern research has shown that the Shark Bay region, in particular, has a fascinating geology and biota. Coupled with its history of European contact (dating back to 1616), it is now considered of international significance and is designated a World Heritage Site.

Dampier the hydrographer

Voyaging in the *Cygnet* in 1688, Captain John Reed, Dampier and their fellow sailors were the first Englishmen to land on mainland Australia. For the north-west coast, and for many other countries and seas that he visited, Dampier's charts and descriptions of weather, currents, coastal conditions including depths and the sea floor, natural history and peoples provided the most important data gathered to that time. Much of the information was brought together in his book *Discourse of Trade-winds, Breezes, Storms, Seasons of the Year, Tides and Currents of the Torrid Zone throughout the World*, published in 1699. He was held in high regard by his British, Dutch, French and Spanish contemporaries, his work being a basis for later expeditions.

Although exploration of the southern hemisphere continued in the eighteenth and nineteenth centuries (including the voyages of Willis, Dalrymple, Cook, Furneaux, Bligh, Vancouver, D'Entrecasteaux, King, etc.), no other explorer visited the west coast of Australia until Baudin in 1801. Two of the many commercial ships of the Dutch East India Company that sailed up the west coast — the *Zuytdorp* in 1712 and the *Zeewijk* in 1727 — were wrecked there, but the survivors of the former lived out their days on the Australian mainland, and those of the latter did not bring back any natural history record. Both Cook (Beaglehole, 1962) and Baudin (1974) made reference to Dampier's observations in their journals. The instructions to Baudin and his fellow captain Hamelin stated that 'In the account of the voyages of Dampier, who twice visited sections of this coast, ... [you] will find comments which may provide useful guidance for this part of [your] navigation. [You] will pay special attention to what the navigators say about the extraordinary tides which occur along the coast'. In his journal, Baudin wrote that, near North West Cape, 'Guided by Dampier's observation and the easterly difference that he experienced [in the wind] in this same area, I steered North by North-West during the night'. Matthew Flinders called Dampier 'our celebrated navigator'.

Dampier's Australian plants

Collection and description

TWENTY-FOUR SPECIES OF AUSTRALIAN PLANTS (including a seaweed) and a number from other countries are represented in Dampier's specimens, now housed in the Fielding–Druce Herbarium at Oxford University in England. How did Dampier collect and dry his specimens? They are well pressed, so evidently he had experience in this practice. All appear to have been broken off rather than cut, even though Dampier almost certainly would have been carrying some kind of knife. Although most are quite resilient plants, even in their flowers, several such as the *Brachycome* wilt quickly once picked, yet these specimens are in a remarkably good state and must have been pressed quite soon after collection. In fact, he used a book for this purpose, as he described after his stay at Bahia on the outward voyage: 'I brought home with me from hence a good Number of Plants, dried between the leaves of Books; of some of the choicest of which, that are not spoil'd, I may give a Specimen at the End of the Book'. Clearly, they were important to him, for they were one of the items saved as the *Roebuck* foundered off Ascension Island on the return voyage and eventually were taken safely to England. It would seem from this statement that he collected more than are now known, but at the end of the voyage discarded those that were in a poor state.

Back home, Dampier handed his collection to Thomas Woodward (1665–1728), Professor of Physics at Gresham College, London. Woodward, in turn, loaned some to John Ray (1627–1705) and others to Leonard Plukenet (1642–1706). Ray, a naturalist and theologian, considered the 'father of British botany', described 18 Dampier plants (nine from Australia, five from Brazil, one from Timor, two from New Guinea, and one from an unknown locality) in his *Historiæ Plantarum* published in 1704. Plukenet was a botanist and physician and became botanist to Queen Mary II as well as superintendent of Hampton Court (Henrey, 1975). He described and illustrated six (probably eight, see below) of Dampier's Australian plants and a number from other countries including Brazil and China in his *Amaltheum Botanicum* published in 1705. ('Amaltheum' is a Latinised word apparently derived from the name of Amalthea who, in Greek mythology, was the foster mother of Zeus and whose name came to mean 'plenty'; as the title of Plukenet's book it presumably denotes a compendium of botanical riches.) In accordance with the practice of the day, the text of both books was in Latin, and what we know as species were circumscribed by phrase names — the practice of using binomial nomenclature (a two-word naming method) for species was not introduced until 1753, when Carl Linnaeus published his *Species Plantarum*. It is unclear why Linnaeus did not take up any of the New Holland plants in this great work, for he adopted many previously described by others, especially those of Ray. He also visited the botanist Johann Jacob Dillenius at Oxford in 1736 (Clokie, 1964) and hence had an opportunity to study the specimens.

The Australian plants described by Ray (in the order in which they appear in his text but with their current names) are:

page 225: *Cystoseira, Hannafordia, Solanum, Conostylis, Sida, Diplolaena, Beaufortia* (also a description of *Centropogon* [as *Rapuntium*] wrongly ascribed to New Holland);

page 226: *Willdampia, Olearia* (also *Casuarina equisetifolia* [as *Equisetum*] wrongly ascribed to New Holland).

Ray, incidentally, was associated with Francis Willughby, the ornithologist and ichthyologist mentioned by Dampier in his account of fishes.

Those described by Plukenet are, in the order in which they appear in his text but with their current names:

page 184: *Adriana* (mistakenly attributed to Brazil); Appendix (unpaginated): *Acacia ligulata*, *Brachycome*, *Thryptomene*, *Dampiera*, *Trachymene*, and probably *Acanthocarpus*; the *Ptilotus* appears only as a figure in plate 441.

Because the names published by Ray and Plukenet predate the formal starting date of modern plant nomenclature, their phrase names are not now accepted. When later botanists named these same plants under the 'modern' system, they used specimens gathered by later collectors in all cases except the *Dampiera*, although several authors mentioned Dampier's journal. When Robert Brown named *Dampiera incana* in 1810, however, he used Dampier's specimens to prepare a description, hence they are the 'type' or original specimens that must be used as the reference point when checking the use of the name.

Ray and Plukenet returned the Dampier specimens to Woodward, who later gave his herbarium to William Sherard (1659–1728), an English botanist who, from about 1680, built up an extensive herbarium at Oxford University (Clokie, 1964). Dampier's precious specimens have remained in the Sherardian Herbarium at the University ever since. Apart from a little insect damage to three specimens (*Adriana*, *Diplolaena*, *Trachymene*) and the loss of several parts (such as some leaves and two capsules from the *Beaufortia*), the specimens are beautifully preserved, virtually as sound today as when Dampier finished drying them. Certainly they can be studied as readily as specimens collected last week.

Not all of Dampier's specimens were studied by Ray and Plukenet, and later research on them has been rather intermittent. Robert Brown examined them, since he chose Dampier's specimens as the type of his species *Dampiera incana* and commented on the specimens of *Diplolaena*. George Bentham cited none in his classic *Flora Australiensis* (1863–78). A list of 14 species was provided by Ferdinand Mueller (1883) but this was based on his interpretation of previous published works and included several errors, notably the determination of Dampier's Plate 1, figure 3 as *Clerodendrum lanceolatum* (it represents a South American plant).

During his term as the first Australian Botanical Liaison Officer at the Royal Botanic Gardens, Kew, in 1937–39, Charles Gardner, then Government Botanist of Western Australia, studied all specimens that were available (17 species) and redetermined them as necessary (Osborn and Gardner, 1939). The grasses were examined jointly with Charles E. Hubbard, of the Kew staff. In the 1950s and 1960s, another Kew botanist, Ronald Melville, made an examination, renaming several. In 1968 I studied them during my term as Botanical Liaison Officer at Kew and reviewed previous research, especially that of Mueller, and Osborn and Gardner (George, 1971). With each study, the nomenclature has been improved, sometimes correcting misidentifications (e.g. *Acacia coriacea*, *Calandrinia polyandra*), sometimes following improved taxonomic understanding (e.g. *Conostylis stylidioides*), some simply changes in the accepted name (e.g. *Myoporum insulare*). Since my account of 1971 there have been ten changes of name for Dampier's plants and two further Australian species are here identified as collected by him. Neville G. Marchant (1988, pp. 194–197) provided a partial account, interpreting the plants mentioned in Dampier's written account of the *Cygnet* voyage of 1688, and the species illustrated in his account of the *Roebuck* voyage of 1699.

Dampier's Australian flowering plant specimens include 23 species in 22 genera from 17 families, and there is one species of seaweed. From his journal we can, with reasonable certainty, recognise a further six species and genera and two families of flowering plants that are not represented by specimens. It is already an interesting cross-section of Australian flora. The largest genus in the flora — *Acacia* — is represented (by two species), as are several of the largest families (*Myrtaceae*, *Fabaceae*, *Poaceae*). Although there are species of the other large Australian genus *Eucalyptus* on Dirk Hartog Island, either Dampier did not find them or he took no specimens. Likewise, another great Australian family, *Proteaceae*, is represented on Dirk Hartog Island by a species of *Grevillea* that today is growing close to his landing place, but there is no specimen among Dampier's collection. Two illustrations in Plukenet almost certainly represent genera not previously recognised as Australian among Dampier's plants — *Acanthocarpus* and *Ptilotus*.

Both Ray and Plukenet described plants collected by Dampier in Brazil. These must have been gathered on the outward voyage, during the stay at Bahia from 4 April to 3 May 1699.

✳

Plant drawings

The identity of the artist responsible for the drawings that appear in Dampier's work *A Voyage to New Holland* is unknown. They were not drawn by Dampier himself, as stated by Stanbury (1987). Gill (1997) suggested that it may have been the clerk James Brand. In the preface Dampier wrote:

> Moreover, which I had not the opportunity of doing in my former Voyages; having now had in the Ship with me a Person skill'd in Drawing, I have by this means been enabled, for the greater Satisfaction of the Curious Reader, to present him with exact Cuts and Figures of several of the principal and most remarkable of those Birds, Beasts, Fishes and Plants, which are described in the following Narrative ... I could have caused many others to be drawn in like manner, but that I resolved to confine my Self to such only, as had some very remarkable difference in the shape of their principal Parts from any that are found in *Europe*.

It was probably the same person who drew the silhouettes of coastlines as seen from the ship. Dampier was probably following a set of instructions prepared by the Royal Society in 1665 for those undertaking long voyages (Smith, 1979). One of these stated that they should 'make Plotts and Draughts of prospects of Coasts, Promontories, Islands and Ports'. It was but a step further to draw plants and animals.

These illustrations are the first published of Australian flora and fauna. Eight species of plants, four birds, five fish, a mammal (dolphin) and a squid or cuttlefish are illustrated in Dampier's *Voyage to New Holland*. One fish (the Old Wife, plate 3, fig. 4) and two plants ('Rapuntium' [= *Centropogon*], tab. 2, fig. 1; 'Equisetum' [= *Casuarina*], tab. 4, fig. 1) were attributed to New Holland but in error (see pp. 146, 147). The plant figures match the dried specimens closely, although since they were drawn, several specimens have suffered either loss of parts (e.g. two fruits missing from the *Beaufortia* [but one now on the sheet with *Hannafordia*], the fruit missing from one *Hannafordia* specimen), or insect damage (especially the larger piece of *Diplolaena* and the *Trachymene*). For their period the drawings are remarkably lifelike. The whereabouts of the originals are unknown. The animals — both birds and marine — are drawn in a different style, almost as though by a different artist. Almost certainly they were drawn on the spot soon after the animals were caught, since no specimens were brought back. On 4 or 5 September, Dampier wrote 'We caught also a Monk-fish, of which I brought home the Picture'.

Other species of Dampier's plants were illustrated by Plukenet (1705). These were copper engravings, from drawings of the pressed specimens by J. Collins, who prepared all 2715 figures in the *Amaltheum* (Stafleu and Cowan, 1983). Five are certainly from Australia (*Adriana*, *Brachycome*, *Acacia ligulata*, *Dampiera* and *Thryptomene*). Two more may be Australian but have not previously been recognised as Dampier's Australian plants. Figure 5 in plate 441 appears to be *Ptilotus villosiflorus* of the family Amaranthaceae. No specimen has been found to match the figure, but an extended caption describes the plant as (translated from Latin) 'a small Amaranthioides with the appearance of a montane, white Polygonum' and attributes it to New Holland. There is no corresponding description in Plukenet's text, but, in a copy of the *Amaltheum* held at Oxford, William Sherard has written the caption on text page 13 where other species of *Amaranthioides* are described, indicating that it was indeed omitted from the printed text. This *Ptilotus* occurs on Dirk Hartog Island close to Dampier's landing site. Further, plate 451, fig. 9 looks remarkably like *Acanthocarpus*, a genus of the family Xanthorrhoeaceae endemic in Western Australia and represented by two species on Dirk Hartog Island. One (*A. robustus*) occurs near Dampier's landing place, but there is no specimen among those now at Oxford. Plukenet described it as (translated) 'a grass from Cheusan with short, sharp leaves bearing globules, producing golden globules, similar to *Chamaemelus nudus*, among the leaves'. Species of *Acanthocarpus* have dry, globular fruits, covered with prickle-like tubercles, that turn golden as they mature. The reference to 'Cheusan' (probably the Chou-Shan islands near Shanghai) is another instance of an incorrect locality being given.

The drawings in Plukenet's work vary in accuracy. Perhaps the best are the *Acanthocarpus* and *Adriana*, though the *Acacia* is also readily recognisable. The *Dampiera* would probably not be recognisable without cross-reference to the text, as the flower has been interpreted as an almost regular corolla, but the figure generally matches one of the specimens at Oxford.

Dampier's plant specimens

In the following account, the 24 extant specimens of plants that Dampier collected are discussed, the flowering plants arranged alphabetically, followed by the seaweed. Most are from Dirk Hartog Island, Shark Bay, but three are from East Lewis Island in the Dampier Archipelago, and the seaweed is probably from an unknown location off the coast. The work of Ray, Plukenet and others who have studied the specimens is discussed, as well as the modern name and other features of the species. Photographs of the specimens are given, accompanied by the figures of those illustrated in Dampier's *Voyage* (1703) and Plukenet's *Amaltheum* (1705). All species are shown in photographs of the plants and their flowers, most taken in approximately the same locality where Dampier saw them.

The herbarium sheets bear no labels in Dampier's hand. The earliest labels are those by Sherard and Plukenet. Various later botanists have added annotations with their comments and re-determinations. Some sheets were not annotated until this century. Labels pertinent to the identification of the specimens are discussed under the species below. Four sheets — those of *Willdampia*, *Dampiera*, that bearing *Thryptomene* and *Melaleuca*, and *Cystoseira* — are shown in full and the various labels are discussed. For the others just the specimens are shown. A scale bar gives centimetres and inches.

In his journal, Dampier described other plants that can be identified. These and others that he almost certainly would have seen are illustrated below.

William Dampier, a portrait painted by Thomas Murray probably in 1698, the year before he left on the voyage to New Holland. Dampier is holding a copy of his first book.

Reproduced courtesy of the National Portrait Gallery, London

Karrakatta Bay, King Sound, where the *Cygnet* was careened on Dampier's first visit to New Holland in January 1688.

Photo: A.S. George

Gum oozing from the trunk of *Eucalyptus dampieri*. Its resemblance to the gum of the Dragon Tree (*Dracaena draco*) of the Canary Islands led to Dampier calling it a Dragon Tree also.

Photo: A.S. George

The bloodwood gum tree *Eucalyptus dampieri*, in a mixed woodland with tall sorghum grass.

Photo: A.S. George

Footprints of a Dingo at Cygnet Bay.

Photo: A.S. George

An English East Indiaman of the early 18th century, thought to be similar to the *Roebuck*.

No illustration of Dampier's ship is known. Painting c.1720 by Peter Monamy (1681–1749).

Reproduced by permission of the National Maritime Museum, Greenwich, London

The west coast of Dirk Hartog Island, a view south from Herald Heights.

Dampier wrote: 'Tis all a steep Shore against the open Sea'.

Photo: A.S. George

Dampier Landing on Dirk Hartog Island where Dampier went ashore in August 1699. In the foreground is the Nitre Bush, *Nitraria billardierei*, that he likened to European samphire. In the background is the barquentine STS *Leeuwin*.

Photo: A.S. George

Another view of Dirk Hartog Island, a little farther inland than the previous photograph, showing the white sand dunes.

Photo: A.S. George

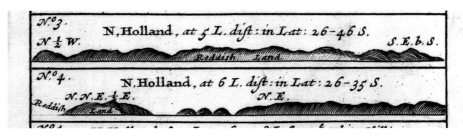

Several coastal profiles, probably drawn by the artist aboard the *Roebuck*. From Dampier (1703),

T. IV, facing p. 117. No. 3 is probably the Zuytdorp Cliffs; No. 4 is probably South Passage with Dirk Hartog Island

to the left and the mainland to the right; No. 7 is south of North West Cape;

Nos. 8, 9 and 10 are in the Dampier Archipelago.

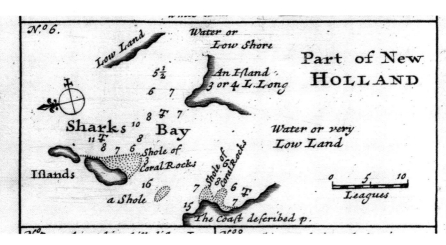

Dampier's map of Shark Bay, from his *Voyage* (1703). North is to the left. At the bottom is

Dirk Hartog Island; at top right is the north end of Peron Peninsula; the 'low land' at top left is

the mainland; at left are Bernier and Dorre Islands. Figures give the sounding depths in fathoms,

and the three anchorages are shown as inverted anchors.

Turtle Bay, just north of Dampier Landing, Dirk Hartog Island. The French explorer François St Allouarn landed on the beach in the foreground in 1772 and left a message in a bottle claiming the western side of New Holland for France.

Photo: A.S. George

A view of the vegetation inland from Dampier Landing on Dirk Hartog Island where Dampier would have walked and collected plants. The flowering shrub is *Beaufortia sprengelioides*.

Photo: A.S. George

Approaching Bernier Island; several of Dampier's crew landed on this island. They found oysters on the rocks along the shore.

Photo: A.S. George

The beach and sand dunes on Bernier Island.

Photo: A.S. George

The spinifex grass *Triodia plurinervata*, the 'Green, short, hard prickly Grass' noticed by Dampier's men on Bernier Island.

Photo: A.S. George

Aerial view over the Lewis Islands, Dampier Archipelago — West Lewis in upper centre, East Lewis top left. Dampier anchored on the further side of East Lewis and landed there, discovering the spectacular flower that would later become known as Sturt Pea. A daisy bush here reminded him of English Rosemary, hence he named this Rosemary Island, but nowadays that name is used for a nearby island.

Photo: K.D. Morris

A view across nearby Enderby Island, showing the natural rock piles characteristic of these islands, described by Dampier as 'Stones ... all of a rusty Colour, and Ponderous'.

Photo: K.D. Morris

Dampier's specimens of Sturt Pea, *Willdampia formosa*. The labels are: upper left, William Sherard, early 18th century, with a line added at the bottom by Johann Jacob Dillenius between 1721 and 1747; middle left, Marmaduke Alexander Lawson, c.1873; bottom left, Ronald Melville, 1958; centre, Humphrey Sibthorp, between 1747 and 1783; bottom centre (written directly on the sheet), unknown; right centre (vertical), Hermia Newman Clokie, c.1960; bottom right, unknown.

Photo: A.S. George

Dampier's probable landing site at Lagrange Bay, with coastal sand dunes in the foreground and the rocky shore exposed at low tide so that 'then there is no Landing with a Boat'.

Photo: A.S. George

The plain just behind the beach at Lagrange Bay, with grey termite mounds that at first reminded Dampier of Hottentot huts in Africa. On examination he decided that they were rocks; they do, indeed, have the texture of soft sandstone-like rock.

Photo: A.S. George

The plain at Lagrange Bay, a little farther inland than the previous photograph, with red termite mounds, and beyond, the low woodland that Dampier described.

Photo: A.S. George

Entrance to a tidal creek at Lagrange Bay, at low tide. The mangroves are mainly *Avicennia marina*.

Photo: A.S. George

John Ray (1627–1705), who described some of Dampier's plant specimens.

JOANNIS RAII,

Societatis Regiæ Socii,

Historiæ Plantarum

TOMUS TERTIUS:

QUI EST

SUPPLEMENTUM

Duorum præcedentium:

Species omnes vel omiſſas, vel poſt Volumina illa evulgata editas, præter innumeras fere novas & indictas ab Amicis communicatas complectens:

CUM

SYNONYMIS neceſſariis,

ET

Uſibus in *Cibo, Medicina,* & *Mechanicis:*

Addito ad Opus conſummandum Generum INDICE copioſo.

ACCESSIT

Hiſtoria Stirpium Inſ. *Luzonis* & reliquarum *Philippinarum*

A

R. P. *Geo. Joſ. Camello,* Moravo-Bruneñſi, S. J. conſcripta.

ITEM

D. *Joſ. Pitton Tournefort,* M.D. Pariſienſis, & in Horto Reg.

BOTANICES PROFESSORIS,

Corollarium Inſtitutionum Rei Herbariæ.

LONDINI:

Apud Sam. Smith & Benj. Walford, Reg. Soc. Typographos, ad Inſignia Principis in Area Boreali D. *Pauli,* cIɔ Iɔ cciv.

Title page of John Ray's *Historiæ Plantarum* (1704).

Plantæ à D. Gulielmo Dampier in Brasilia, Nova Hollandia, Timor & Nova Guinea, observatæ & collectæ.

Brasilianæ.

1. *Flos Cotoniferus*, E plurimis filamentis conftat, pilorum ferè tenuitate, 4 uncias longis, colore purpurafcente, apicibus cinereis capitatis. Flavis pediculus ad exortum quinque anguftis rigidis foliis, fex circiter uncias longis cingitur.

2. *Jafminum Brafilianum luteum, mali Limoniæ folio nervofo, petalis craffis.*

3. *Crifta Pavonis* Brafiliana *Bardanæ foliis.* Folia valde tenera funt, Bardanæ majoris fummis foliis fimilia quoad formam & texturam.

4. *Filix* Brafiliana *Ofmundæ minori ferrato folio.* Filix hæc ex earum genere eft quæ vafcula feminalia in lineis foliorum margines ambientibus proferunt.

Novæ Hollandiæ.

1. *Rapuntium* Novæ Hollandiæ, *flore magno coccineo.* Perianthium è 5 longis acuminatis partibus componitur. Vafculi feminalis forma, feminum parvitas, Floris figura irregularis, & foliorum tenuitas hanc plantam Rapuntium effe arguunt.

2. *Fucus foliis capillaceis breviffimis, veficulis minimis donatis.* Fucus hic elegans ex Ericæ marinæ feu *Sargazo* genere eft, verùm partium minorum & tenuiorum.

3. *Ricinoides* Novæ Hollandiæ *angulofo craffo folio.* Hæc planta fruticofa eft, foliis craffis tomentofis, latere præfertim inferiore. Fructus tricoccus, exteriùs incanus, calice in 5 partes divifo. Ad Ricinum fructu parvo, fruticofum folio Phylli *P. B. P.* accedit.

4. *Solanum fpinofum* N^{væ} Hollandiæ, *foliis Phylli fubrotundis.* Florem profert cœrulefcentem, aliorum congenerum fimilem. Folia colore funt albicante, craffa & utrinque lanuginofa, unciam propemodum longa, & tantundem ferè lata. Spinæ acutiffimæ funt & creberrimæ, Aurantii colore intenfo, præfertim prope cufpides.

9. *Equifetum* Novæ Hollandiæ *frutefcens foliis longiffimis.* An vera & genuina Equifeti fpecies fit hæc planta dubito, verùm quia folia pyxidatim articulata funt Equifetorum inftar ad hoc Genus eam retuli.

10. *Colutea* Novæ Hollandiæ floribus amplis coccineis, umbellatim difpofitis, maculâ purpureâ notatis. Folia fpecimini noftro defunt, unde ad quod Genus propriè pertineat non facilè eft determinare. Flores Coluteæ Barbæ Jovis folio, flore coccineo *Breynii* perfimiles funt, ejufdem coloris coccinei, cum macula ampla intensè purpurea in vexillo, fed multò majores, omnes ab eodem puncto provenientes umbellæ in modum. Siliquæ rudimentum valde lanuginofum eft, & in filamentum duas uncias longum terminatur.

11. *Conyza* Novæ Hollandiæ *anguftis Rofmarini foliis.* Hæc planta valde ramofa eft, & lignea effe videtur. Flores perbrevibus pediculis infiftunt, è foliorum finubus ortis. Folia autem Rorifmarini exactè fimilia funt, duntaxat minora.

Pages 225 and 226 of Ray's *Historiæ Plantarum* with Latin descriptions of Dampier's New Holland plants.

LEONHARDUS PLUKENET.

*Ein berühmter Englaendischer Botaniker, der sich zu London zu Ausgang des 17¹
Jahrhunderts bekañt machte, und zu Anfang des 18. Jahrhunderts starb.*

Leonard Plukenet (1642–1706), who described and illustrated some of Dampier's plant specimens.

Courtesy of the Hunt Institute for Botanical Documentation, Carnegie Mellon University, Pittsburgh, Pennsylvania

LEONARDI PLUKENETII

AMALTHEUM BOTANICUM.

(i. e.)

Stirpium Indicarum Alterum

COPIÆ CORNU

Millenas ad minimum & bis centum diverfas Species novas & indictas nomi-
natim comprehendens; Quarum Sexcenæ & infuper, Selectis Iconibus,

ÆNEISQUE TABULIS

In gratiam Phytofophorum exquifitè & fummo artificio
Illuftrantur.

Opus TEMPORI Sacratum.

In Magnis vel Voluiffe Sat eft.

M. Vander Gucht. fa.

Plurimum ad Inveniendum contulit, qui fperavit poffe reperiri.
Pigri eft Ingenii contentum effe his, quæ ab aliis inventa funt.

Senec. Epift. 80.

LONDINI M.DCC.V.

1705

Title page of Leonard Plukenet's *Amaltheum Botanicum* (1705).

limi folio *Breyn. Prodr.* 2. 99. Hujus pictura exstat in *Phytogr. tab.* 107. *fig.* 6.

R Icinus *Maderaspatanus*, Marrubii albi foliis, fructu tri-cocco inter folia disperso.

Ricinus *Ind. Or.* foliis quinquifidis, subtùs lanugine obsi-tis; Paretty-maram *Malabarorum.*

Ricinus *Brasiliensis*, Geranii nodosi folio trifido; inter Collectaneas D. *Dampier.*

Ricinus *Maderaspatanus*, folio trifido, & quinquifido mol-lioribus spinulis, cum suis globulis coronatis, in ambitu ornato, Cautamanuck *Malabarorum.*

Ricinus Saniculæ, s. Diapensiæ folio *Sinarum*, ex Insula *Cheusán.*

Unnumbered page of the Appendix of Plukenet's *Amaltheum Botanicum* with Latin descriptions
of Dampier's New Holland plants.

APPENDIX.

Frutex Nov'eboracensis, Elæagni foliis brevioribus minutissime crenatis, fructu parvo quinquecapsulari.

Frutex *Sinensis* alatis foliis siliquosus, torosis siliquis, villis aureis densius obductis.

Frutex *Sinensis* Senæ sylvestris folio angustiori, nodosa siliqua rostro longiore donata.

Fruticulus *Nov'eboracensis*, hirsutis Myrti minoribus foliis, capsulis parvis tricarpos.

Fruticulus verticillatus Prunifolio longiore *Brasilianus.* Eundem etiam habuimus e *Terra Mariana.*

Fucus ramulis compressiusculis crusta aurea sanguineis guttis duplici utrinque ordine insignita obsitis, ex *Guinea.* Corallina lutea punctorum rubentium duplici utrinque phalange insignita, *Doctoris Woodward.*

G

GRamen parvum *Cheusanense* spicatum, granulis compressis cordiformibus.
Gramen *Cheusanicum* foliis brevibus aculeatis globuliferum, globulos aureos Chamæmeli nudi similes inter folia proferens.

J

JAsminum *Brasilianum* Lauri folium, floribus longo tubulo donatis.

L

LAserpitium Apii paludosi folio *Marilandicum.*
Leucoium maritimum *Nov'hollandicum,* folio parvo incano, flore amplo cæruleo.
Lotoides *Æthiopicum* Saxifragæ pratensis folio, multifariam in quinque partes diviso.

M

MAlva *Brasiliana,* angustis lanuginosis, & serratis foliis, flore aureo parvo.
Melissa *Brasilica,* subrotundis parvis foliis inodora.
Mespilus Oxyacantha dictus *Cheusanensis* oblongis, mucronatis, & serratis foliis, fructu longiore, summis ramulis innascente.
Mespilus Oxyacantha dictus *Nov'eboracensis,* Rosæ sativæ foliis, fructu parvo rotundo, inter folia sparso.
Muscus denticulatus major, ex *Ceram,* Insula *Amboinæ* adjacente.
Muscus denticulatus minor, ex Insula *Cheusan.*

N

NUmmularia (forte) crenatis foliis. An Veronica pratensis Nummulariæ foliis, Planta repens *Brasiliana* ?

P

PErsicariæ folio planta *Cheusanica,* fructu parvo rotundiore, summo caule in spicam disposito.

R

R Hus trifoliatum *Brasilianum,* foliis glabris.
Ricinus *Nov'hollandicus* triphyllos, capsulis eleganter bullatis.

S

SOlanum *Brasilianum,* folio integro, mucronato, glabro, Papas *Americani* floribus in summitate caulis.

V

VIola surrecta *Virginiana,* Xylostii foliis, flosculorum petalis eleganter crenatis.

UMbelliferis adsinis, Ranunculi folio, planta pusilla, *Hollandiæ Novæ.*

I N D E X.

Unnumbered page of the Appendix of Plukenet's *Amaltheum Botanicum* with Latin descriptions of Dampier's New Holland plants.

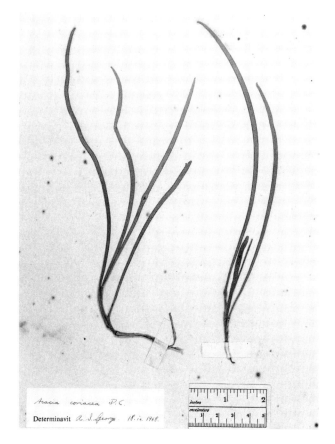

Acacia coriacea.

Dampier's specimens.

Photo: A.S. George

Acacia coriacea, shrub (left), foliage and pods (right).

Photos: A.S. George

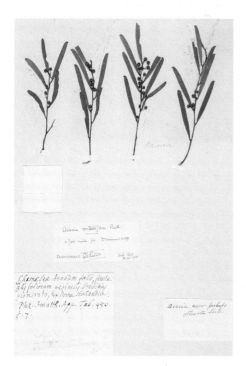

Acacia ligulata. Left, Dampier's specimens. Right, figure from Plukenet, *Amaltheum Botanicum*, Plate 450, fig. 7.

Photo courtesy of the Department of Plant Sciences, University of Oxford

Acacia ligulata, shrub.

Photo: B.R. Maslin

Acacia ligulata, flowers and foliage.

Photo: A.S. George

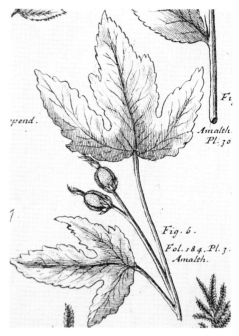

Adriana tomentosa. Above, Dampier's specimens.

Right, figure from Plukenet, *Amaltheum Botanicum*,

Plate 453, fig. 6.

Photo: A.S. George

Adriana tomentosa, shrub (above), maturing fruit (above right), male flowers (lower right).

Photos: G.J. Keighery, S. van Leeuwen

Beaufortia sprengelioides. Left, Dampier's specimen. Right, figure from his *Voyage to New Holland,* tab. 3, fig. 4.

Photo: A.S. George

Beaufortia sprengelioides, shrub (left) and flowers (right).

Photos: A.S. George

Calandrinia polyandra. Left, Dampier's specimen. *Brachycome* aff. *cheilocarpa*. Centre, right, Dampier's specimens.

Photo: A.S. George

Calandrinia polyandra.

Photo: A.S. George

Brachycome aff. *cheilocarpa*.

Photo: A.S. George

Brachycome aff. *cheilocarpa*.

Figure from Plukenet, *Amaltheum Botanicum*, Plate 450, fig. 10.

Conostylis stylidioides. Left, Dampier's specimens. Right, figure from his *Voyage to New Holland*, Tab. 3, fig. 1.

Photo: A. S. George

Conostylis stylidioides, plant (left) and flowers (right).

Photos: A.S. George

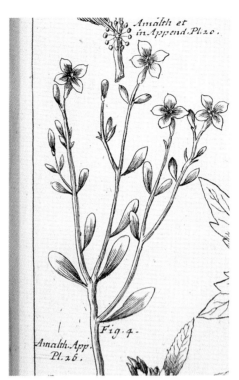

Dampiera incana. Left, Dampier's specimens. The labels are: upper left and lower right, William Sherard, early 18th century; lower left, Charles A. Gardner, 1937. Right, figure from Plukenet, *Amaltheum Botanicum*, Plate 451, fig. 4.

Photo courtesy of the Department of Plant Sciences, University of Oxford

Dampiera incana, plant, with new growth on the left that will produce next year's flowers — as in Dampier's lower left specimen.

Photo: A.S. George

Dampiera incana, flowers.

Photo: A.S. George

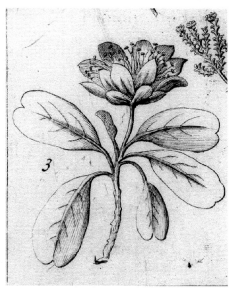

Diplolaena grandiflora. Left, Dampier's specimens. Right, figure from his *Voyage to New Holland*, Tab. 3, fig. 3.

Photo: A.S. George

Diplolaena grandiflora, shrub (above);
flowers and foliage (right).

Photos: A.S. George

Frankenia pauciflora.

Dampier's specimens.

Photo: A.S. George

Frankenia pauciflora, plant (left) and flower (right).

Photos: A.S. George

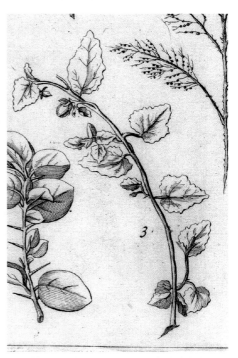

Hannafordia quadrivalvis.

Above, Dampier's specimens. Right, figure from his *Voyage to New Holland*, Tab. 2, fig. 3.

Photo: A.S. George

Hannafordia quadrivalvis, plant (left), flower and fruit (right).

Photos: A.S. George

Lotus cruentus.

Dampier's specimen.

Photo: A.S. George

Lotus cruentus, plant (left) and flowers (right).

Photos: A.S. George

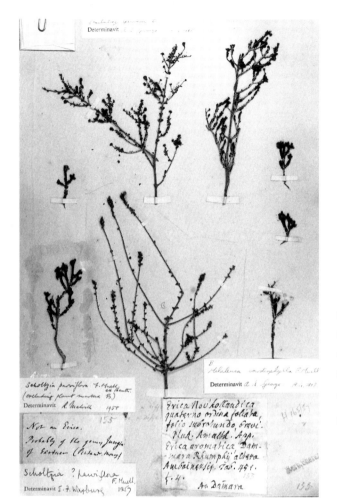

Melaleuca cardiophylla.
Dampier's specimens —
the large spindly specimen
labelled 'B' at lower centre;
the others are all *Thryptomene*.
See page 79 for explanation
of labels.

Photo: A.S. George

Melaleuca cardiophylla, plant (left), buds and fruit (right).

Photos: A.S. George

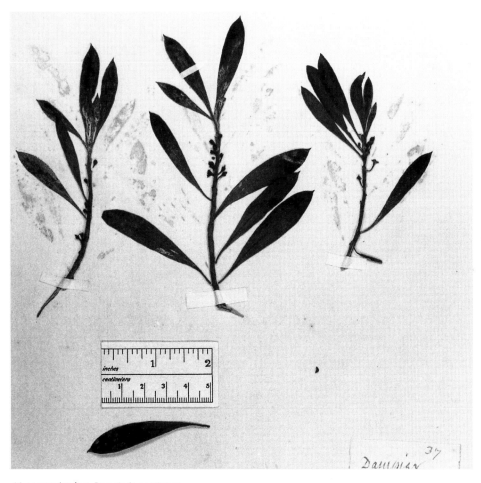

Myoporum insulare. Dampier's specimens.

Photo: A.S. George

Myoporum insulare, plant (left),
flowers and young fruit (right).

Photos: A.S. George

Olearia 'dampieri'. Left, Dampier's specimens. Right, figure from his *Voyage to New Holland*, Tab. 4, fig. 3.

Photo of Dampier's specimens courtesy of the Department of Plant Sciences, University of Oxford

Olearia 'dampieri', shrub (left); foliage and seeding heads (right).

Photos: A.A. Burbidge

Paractaenum novaehollandiae. Dampier's specimen.

Photo: A.S. George

Paractaenum novaehollandiae, plant (above right),

flowers (lower right).

Photos: A.S. George

Pittosporum phylliraeoides. Dampier's specimens.

Photo: A.S. George

Pittosporum phylliraeoides, shrub (left), flowers and foliage (right).

Photos: A.S. George

In the following accounts the heading gives the current botanical name, the person who gave it that name, the year published, and the family to which the species belongs.

Acacia coriacea A.P. de Candolle (1825) Mimosaceae
Wirewood

The generic name *Acacia* is an ancient one, having been used by the Greek physician Pedanius Dioscorides (c. 20–70) for some prickly wattles from Egypt. Strangely it was not published by Linnaeus in his *Species Plantarum* (1753), the first modern usage being by the English botanist Philip Miller in 1754.

This species was named in 1825 by the Swiss botanist Augustin Pyramus de Candolle from specimens collected during a stay at Shark Bay in June–July 1801 on the voyage of Nicholas Baudin (although de Candolle stated, wrongly, that the specimens were from the east coast). The epithet *coriacea* (Latin, leathery) refers to the texture of the phyllodes.

Dampier's specimens are sterile and were left unnamed until 1939 when Charles Gardner determined them as *Grevillea pyramidalis*, with a slight reservation (indicated by a question mark in his annotation with the specimens). He seems to have misinterpreted the cluster of phyllodes as the divided leaf typical of that species of *Grevillea*, although a close examination would have revealed the different venation, not to mention the small pulvinus present at the base of the phyllodes in many species of wattle. I recognised it as *Acacia coriacea* in 1968. Cowan and Maslin (1993) recognised three sub-species in *A. coriacea*: subsp. *coriacea* (Dampier's collection) grows along the coast from Shark Bay north to Point Samson; subsp. *pendens* occurs from the north-west coast inland through the Pilbara; and subsp. *sericophylla* is wide-spread though inland regions of all States except Victoria.

This is a spreading, bushy shrub to 3 metres tall with long, silvery phyllodes, cream flowers and curved pods 15–30 cm long. During our visit to Dirk Hartog Island in August 1998, some bushes were in leaf only, others bore almost-mature pods, but we do not know if Dampier also saw pods.

Acacia ligulata A. Cunningham ex G. Bentham (1842) Mimosaceae

The name of this species was suggested by the collector of the type specimens, Allan Cunningham, and published by the British botanist George Bentham, hence the 'ex' between their names. Cunningham collected his specimens (which are in fruit) on Dirk Hartog Island on 21 January 1822 (Chapman and Maslin, 1992), during a coastal survey voyage with Phillip Parker King. The Latin epithet *ligulata* (tongue-like) refers to the shape of the phyllodes — broadly oblong. This is one of the most common wattles of arid Australia, growing on dunes from the central west coast through the inland regions of all mainland States. It is a bushy shrub or small tree, usually flowering profusely in spring.

Dampier's specimens are in full flower, and the shrubs must have made a colourful showing at the time of his visit. Plukenet (Appendix, plant 5, tab. 450, fig. 7) described the plant as 'Chamæleæ Arabum' and misinterpreted the flower heads as fruit ('with clustered fruit on short pedicels from the angles of the leaves'). A colour photograph of Dampier's specimens was given by Steven (1988). They have previously been identified as *Acacia rostellifera* G. Bentham, a closely related species.

Adriana tomentosa C. Gaudichaud-Beaupré (1825) Euphorbiaceae

This species was named by Charles Gaudichaud at the same time as he published the name of the genus. *Adriana* commemorates the French botanist Adrien de Jussieu (1797–1853), son of Antoine de Jussieu (1748–1836) who developed a 'natural' system of classifying plants. The epithet *tomentosa* (Latin *tomentosus*, covered with short, dense hairs) refers to the leaves and stems. Gaudichaud himself collected specimens at Shark Bay in 1818 during the voyage of Louis de Freycinet, 1817–20. Two varieties are now recognised in the species, this being var. *tomentosa*, and the other var. *hookeri* of the inland deserts.

The species is dioecious, i.e. it has male and female flowers on separate plants. In both sexes there is an inconspicuous green calyx and no petals. The male flowers have yellow stamens and the females reddish-orange stigmas. Dampier's specimens include female flowers. Plukenet (Appendix, tab. 453, fig. 6) was correct in relating them to *Ricinus* of the family Euphorbiaceae, but decided that they were the same as a Brazilian plant. He compared the leaf shape to that of a geranium.

The locality where Dampier collected this species is uncertain. The species occurs from Kalbarri to Broome and inland to the desert margin. There has been no other collection from Dirk Hartog Island or from Bernier Island, but it is recorded for islands of the Dampier Archipelago, hence it is likely that the specimen was collected on East Lewis Island.

Beaufortia sprengelioides (A.P. de Candolle) Craven (1999) Myrtaceae
Melaleuca sprengelioides A.P. de Candolle (1827)

Dampier's specimen was described by Ray as 'Dammara ex Nova Hollandia, sanamundae secundae Clusii foliis', i.e. dammar from New Holland with leaves resembling those of Clusius' sanamunda. In his English account, Dampier quaintly translated Ray's description of the leaves 'per paria opposita' as 'answering one another cross-ways'. The inclusion in a group called dammara was presumably on account of the oil glands in the leaves, although the fruit also resembles that of *Melaleuca leucadendra* which the contemporary botanist Georg Rumphius called dammara. The name was also widely used for species of pine. Dammars are resins obtained from a number of tropical trees, commonly used in varnishes and other products (Mabberley, 1987). Dampier mentioned obtaining 'Dammer for my Ship' at Timor. 'Sanamunda' is a plant of the family Thymelaeaceae with purgative qualities, occurring in Spain and southern France.

Beaufortia was named by Robert Brown in 1814 after Mary, Duchess of Beaufort (1630–1714) who had large gardens at Badminton and Chelsea. The species collected by Dampier has been known for many years as *Beaufortia dampieri*, but the species was first named in 1827 as a *Melaleuca* by Augustin de Candolle. His description was not associated with *Beaufortia* until 1998, by Lyn Craven during his research into the genus *Melaleuca*, and he recently published the combination in *Beaufortia* (Craven, 1999). The epithet *sprengelioides* refers to a presumed resemblance of the plant to species of *Sprengelia*, a genus of Epacridaceae.

Previous researchers did not associate de Candolle's name with a Western Australian plant since his description was brief and he wrongly gave the east coast of Australia as the locality. Allan Cunningham gave the manuscript name 'Dampieri' to the specimens that he collected on Dirk Hartog Island between 21 and 25 January 1822, and this was taken up by William Hooker when he published a description. Cunningham chose to commemorate Dampier in the specific epithet, but whether he was aware that the latter had collected it is unknown.

This low, spreading shrub is common inland from Dampier's landing site and, although less colourful than most other species of the genus, forms quite a prominent display. The leaves are 2–3 mm long and the flower heads about 20 mm across. The outer flowers of the head are male and the inner ones bisexual, hence only the latter develop fruits, which are woody capsules 7–8 mm long. It also occurs on the mainland as far south as the Murchison River. Occasionally the flowers are cream or white. Dirk Hartog Island represents the northernmost occurrence of *Beaufortia*.

Between the time when the drawing was made and now, the specimen has lost two fruits (one now on the sheet with *Hannafordia*) and several leaves.

Brachycome aff. *cheilocarpa* F. Mueller (1882) Asteraceae

This is one of the specimens described and illustrated by Plukenet (Appendix, tab. 450, fig. 10), as a very small Chrysanthemum. He correctly placed it with what we know as the Asteraceae (daisy family).

The modern generic name, published by the French botanist Alexandre-Henri de Cassini in 1816, is taken from the Greek *brachys* (short) and *come* (hair), in reference to the ring of hairs on the top of the fruit of most species. This species was named by the Australian botanist Ferdinand Mueller from specimens collected by John Forrest near the Gascoyne River, Western Australia, probably in winter or spring 1882. The specific epithet *cheilocarpa* (Greek *cheilos*, a lip or beak, and *carpos*, a fruit) refers to the tip of the fruit. Recent research has shown that the plants in the Shark Bay region belong to a complex around this species, and further study is in train to resolve their classification (Philip Short, pers. comm., 1998).

This is a group of annual daisies widespread in the semi-arid regions of central and north-west Western Australia. They grow to about 20–30 cm tall and have flower heads 1.5–2.5 cm across. The outer flowers with the purple 'ray' petals are female, those of the disc tubular, yellow and bisexual. The fruits that develop from these disc flowers are small and nut-like.

Dampier's specimens (which were missing when Osborn and Gardner made their study in 1937–39) are in flower and would have been one of the plants that he referred to as 'some very small Flowers, growing on the Ground, that were sweet and beautiful'.

Calandrinia polyandra (W.J. Hooker) G. Bentham (1863) Portulacaceae
Parakeelya

Calandrinia was named in 1816 by a German botanist, Carl Sigismund Kunth, after Jean Luis Calandrini (1703–1758), a professor of botany and mathematics in Geneva. The prominent British botanist William Hooker first named this species in 1855, based on specimens grown in a glasshouse at the Royal Botanic Gardens, Kew, in 1854. These had been raised from seed collected in Western Australia by James Drummond, probably on his expedition to the Murchison River in 1850–51. It was called *Talinum polyandrum* by Hooker but George Bentham transferred it to *Calandrinia* in 1863. The specific epithet is from the Greek *poly-* (many) and *andrus* (in botany, a stamen), each flower having many stamens. Dampier's specimen was determined as *Calandrinia liniflora* E. Fenzl by Ronald Melville at Kew in 1956 and so listed by George (1971).

This is an ephemeral herb with succulent leaves and delicate flowers that each open for one day only. A small capsule develops containing many black seeds. The species is common along the central west coast and nearby parts of Western Australia and makes a colourful display on sunny spring days. It is another of Dampier's 'very small Flowers, growing on the Ground, that were sweet and beautiful'. Neither Ray nor Plukenet seems to have studied this specimen.

Conostylis stylidioides F. Mueller (1873) Haemodoraceae
Cottonheads

The name *Conostylis* was coined by Robert Brown in 1810 from the Greek *conos* (a cone) and *stylos* (a column, hence style of a flower), in reference especially to the shape of the style base in the genus.

Mueller described the species from specimens that Augustus Oldfield collected near the lower Murchison River, probably in the 1860s. The epithet *stylidioides* refers to the similarity in habit to some species of *Stylidium* (triggerplants). The species occurs from the Geraldton area north to Dirk Hartog Island.

Dampier's specimen was called a Scabiosa by Ray and recognised as *Conostylis* by Charles Gardner (1939). His determination as *C. candicans* var. *leptophylla* G. Bentham was accepted until research showed that this name applies to a natural hybrid of occasional occurrence, and that the species on Dirk Hartog Island is *C. stylidioides* (Hopper et al., 1987). The island is the northernmost locality for the genus, which is endemic in south-western Australia.

The drawing matches the left-hand specimen (reversed) which seems to have lost a few flowers over the years.

Dampiera incana R. Brown (1810) Goodeniaceae
Hoary Dampiera

This was described by Plukenet as 'Leucoium maritimum Nov. hollandicum, fol. parvo, incano, fl. amplo, caeruleo', i.e. a seaside Leucoium from New Holland, with a small hoary leaf, a large blue flower. Since 1753 the name *Leucojum* has been used for the snowflake, but in Plukenet's day it seems to have been used simply for a white plant with purple or blue flowers (it is derived from the Greek *leukon*, white, and *ion*, violet) (Smith, 1972).

In naming the genus, Brown wrote 'Genus ... dixi in memoriam GULIELMI DAMPIER, navarchi et peregrinatoris celeberrimi, in variis suis itineribus naturae semper assidui observatoris, nec botanicem neglegentis, qui oram occidentalem Novae Hollandiae bis visitavit, cujus regionis plantae aliquae depictae in relatione itineris exstant, et inter ineditas secum reportatas (quarum plures nunc in Museo Oxoniensi asservantur), *Dampiera incana* fuit'; i.e. I have named the genus in memory of William Dampier, the very famous captain and traveller, on his various journeys always an assiduous observer of nature, not neglecting the botany, who twice visited the west coast of New Holland, of which region illustrations of some plants appear in the account of his journey, and among the unpublished specimens brought back (many of which are now in the Oxford Museum) was *Dampiera incana*'. The specific epithet (Latin *incanus*, hoary) refers to the grey hairs covering most of the plant. Besides the specimens at Oxford, there is a piece at the Natural History Museum, South Kensington, probably donated in Brown's time.

This is a perennial herb with grey felted leaves and spikes of deep blue, unscented flowers. It occurs through the north-west of Western Australia and south to Geraldton, usually growing in sandy soil in heath or shrubland, and flowering in late winter and spring. This plant epitomises the blue flowers that so impressed Dampier in New Holland.

Diplolaena grandiflora R.L. Desfontaines (1817) Rutaceae
Wild Rose

This plant puzzled John Ray who described it thus (in the English translation, Dampier 1703): 'Of what genus this Shrub or Tree is, is uncertain, agreeing with none yet describ'd, as far as can be judg'd, by the State it is in. It has a very beautiful Flower, of a red colour as far as can be guess'd by the dry *Specimen*, consisting of ten large *Petala*, hoary on both sides, especially underneath; the middle of the Flower is thick set with *Stamina*, which are woolly at the bottom, the length of the *Petala*, each of them crown'd with its *Apex*. The *Calix* is divided into five round pointed parts. The Leaves are like those of *Amelanchier Lob.* green a Top and very woolly underneath, not running to a point, as is common in others, but with an Indenture at the upper-end'. Apart from taking this to be a single flower, much of this description is surprisingly accurate to modern eyes.

Amelanchier is a north-temperate genus of the rose family. 'Lob.' refers to the botanist and physician Matthias de Lobel, born in Flanders in 1538, died in London in 1616, after whom the genus *Lobelia* is named. Since the modern system of naming plants began in 1753, however, Lobel is no longer associated with the botanical name *Amelanchier*, rather Friedrich Medikus who first published it under the new system in 1789.

The modern generic name *Diplolaena* was given by Robert Brown, from the Greek *diploös* (double) and *chlaina* (a cloak), in reference to the two rows of bracts around the flowers. Brown had studied Dampier's specimens and illustration. The species was named in 1817 by the French botanist René Louiche Desfontaines from specimens collected by Leschenault de la Tour on the Baudin expedition in 1801 on the 'Iles Stériles' (Bernier and Dorre Islands) off the west coast of 'terre d'Endracht' (Western Australia). The epithet is derived from the Latin *grandis* (large) and *flos* (a flower), this having larger heads than the other species. Desfontaines also referred to the description in Dampier's *Voyage to New Holland*. The species occurs from Geraldton to Shark Bay and also at Yardie Creek near North West Cape; it is common on the Abrolhos Islands.

One of Dampier's specimens has been damaged by insects.

In an odd twist, Desfontaines named another species *Diplolaena dampieri* which he believed was the same species that Dampier collected, and this name was used for the Shark Bay plant for many years. In fact, his type specimen of *D. dampieri* is a species that occurs at Cape Naturaliste, in the far south-west of the continent (Wilson, 1998).

Frankenia pauciflora A.P. de Candolle (1824) var. *pauciflora* Frankeniaceae
Seaheath

Dampier's specimens were not studied, or at least not described or annotated, by the early botanists. Indeed, these were not named until 1938 when the English botanist Victor Summerhayes recognised them as a species of *Frankenia*.

The genus received its modern name from Carl Linnaeus in 1753, commemorating Johann Franke (1590–1661), professor of botany and anatomy at Uppsala, Sweden. He wrote one of the first scientific accounts of Swedish plants. This species was named in 1824 by French botanist Augustin Pyramus de Candolle from a specimen collected at Shark Bay in 1801 on the Baudin voyage. The epithet is from the Latin *paucus* (few) and *flos* (a flower), the flowers usually being rather sparse in this species.

This low, sprawling small shrub is a common coastal plant from north-western Australia to Victoria, but also grows on saline flats inland in Western and South Australia, Victoria and New South Wales. It is probably one of the plants on Dirk Hartog Island that reminded Dampier of 'Heath, much of the kind we have growing on our Commons in England', but it is also at Lagrange Bay. A species of seaheath, *Frankenia laevis*, is common in coastal marshes of south-eastern England.

Hannafordia quadrivalvis F. Mueller (1860) Sterculiaceae

This was described by Ray as 'Ricinoides Novæ Hollandiæ, anguloso, crasso folio', i.e. [A plant] 'like Ricinus of New Holland, with an angular thick leaf'. The association with *Ricinus* (the castor oil plant) is incorrect, as they have very different flowers and fruit. *Ricinus* is now placed in the family Euphorbiaceae, and Dampier's plant in the Sterculiaceae.

Ferdinand Mueller, a German migrant who became one of Australia's greatest botanists, described *Hannafordia* in 1860. The name commemorates Samuel Hannaford, a journalist who collected plants in Victoria. The specimens named by Mueller were collected by J. Walcott and Augustus Oldfield near the lower Murchison River, Western Australia, in the 1850s. At the time this was the only species known. The specific epithet is derived from the Latin *quadri-* (four-) and *-valvis* (derived from *valvae*, folding doors, and hence the valves of a fruit that splits open), in reference to the fruit. There are now three species in the genus, all confined to Australia. They are small, rather inconspicuous shrubs, velvety with a covering of stellate hairs. The pale yellow flower is bell-like and pendulous, followed by a spherical dry fruit that splits open to release a few seeds.

Hannafordia quadrivalvis occurs in kwongan (heath) between Shark Bay and the lower Murchison River, as well as a few localities to the south-east. An unnamed subspecies grows farther north, between the Minilya River and North West Cape.

The fruit shown in Dampier's figure (drawn from the left-hand specimen) has disappeared from the specimen since it was drawn. The drawing was mistakenly called *Adriana tomentosa* by Scott-Child (1992).

Lotus cruentus A.B. Court (1957) Fabaceae
Redflower Lotus

Dampier's specimen (which bears no flowers) lay unnamed until 1938, when Charles Gardner studied it and thought that it might be a species of *Tephrosia*, a genus of herbaceous pea flowers with many species in northern Australia. He indicated his uncertainty with a question mark before the name. When I saw the specimen in 1968 I recognised it as *Lotus cruentus*, an ephemeral pea that occurs widely through the arid and semi-arid regions of Australia. It is highly variable, commonly having wider leaflets than those of plants in the Shark Bay area.

The species was originally named *Lotus coccineus* by the German botanist Diederich von Schlechtendal in 1848, based on a collection by Hans Hermann Behr from South Australia. The epithet *coccineus* had already been used in *Lotus* (in 1825) for a different species, hence Schlechtendal's name could not be retained and Arthur Court published the new epithet *cruentus*, a Latin word meaning blood-red, in reference to the petals, thus retaining Schlechtendal's original meaning.

Dampier's specimen of this attractive annual matches other specimens from the Shark Bay area in its leaves, and the species is common where he landed on Dirk Hartog Island.

Melaleuca cardiophylla F. Mueller (1859) Myrtaceae
Tangling Melaleuca

Melaleuca is one of Carl Linnaeus' botanical names, published in 1767. The name is derived from the Greek *melas* (black) and *leucos* (white), apparently in reference to the colour of the bark of the first species named. Ferdinand Mueller described this species from a collection gathered by Augustus Oldfield from Port Gregory, just north of Geraldton. The epithet is from the Greek *cardia* (a heart) and *phyllon* (a leaf) and refers to the leaf shape. The species is common in places along the Western Australian coast from Perth to North West Cape, and on Barrow Island. On Dirk Hartog Island it is a rather sprawling shrub. In August it is in bud, hence Dampier's specimen is not flowering. The white flowers are in small clusters along the stems and later form small woody capsules containing several seeds.

On the herbarium sheet at Oxford, this species is mounted with *Thryptomene baeckeacea*, suggesting that at one time the specimens may have been considered all the one species. Plukenet studied the *Thryptomene* (q.v.) but there is no indication that he saw the *Melaleuca*.

Myoporum insulare R. Brown (1810) Myoporaceae
Blueberry Tree, Boobialla

This was listed as *Myoporum montanum* R. Brown by Mueller (1883), and as *Myoporum acuminatum* R. Brown by Osborn and Gardner (1939) and George (1971). Both are now considered synonyms of *M. insulare*.

The genus *Myoporum* was published in 1786 by Johann Georg Adam Forster, taking the name coined by Daniel Solander (who accompanied Joseph Banks on the *Endeavour* voyage of 1768–71). The name is derived from the Greek *myo* (to close or shut), and *poros* (a pore), in reference to the glands of the leaves.

The specific epithet is from the Latin *insularis* (of an island) and refers to the locality where Brown gathered his type collection — the Kent Islands in Bass Strait, collected in December 1804.

This large shrub occurs around much of the coastline of Australia, from the Kimberley around the southern coast to Queensland. It has small tubular white flowers with purple spots inside, and the fruit is a purple berry, possibly one of those referred to by Dampier in his account of the plants on Dirk Hartog Island.

Dampier did well to dry his specimens relatively intact, for this species has a tendency to shed its leaves as they dry.

Olearia 'dampieri' (A. Cunningham ex A.P. de Candolle)
new combination to be made Asteraceae
Eurybia dampieri A. Cunningham ex A.P. de Candolle

This is the plant that, in the shape of its leaves, reminded Dampier of the English Rosemary (*Rosmarinus officinalis*), even though it did not have any scent when he crushed it. Curiously, in some localities it does have a scent, according to notes with modern herbarium specimens. Ray described Dampier's specimen as a *Conyza* (a name now used for a related group of daisies) with the narrow leaves of Rosemary, and wrote 'It tasts very bitter now dry'. It is appropriate that, when he found the same plant in 1818, Allan Cunningham decided to coin an epithet commemorating Dampier. He used it only in his manuscript, but Augustin de Candolle took it up when he described the new species in 1836. Cunningham also collected his specimens in the Dampier Archipelago, on Enderby Island. At that period, the generic name in use was *Eurybia*. Most species published under this name were later transferred to *Olearia*, but by then this one was considered the same as *O. axillaris*, hence there was no need for the name to be used. Recent research has shown that this narrow-leaved shrub is indeed a distinct species, and the transfer of the name *dampieri* to *Olearia* will be made shortly (N.S. Lander, pers. comm., 1998). The combination is used informally here.

The generic name *Olearia* was published in 1802 by the German botanist Conrad Moench. It is thought to be derived from the Greek *olea*, the Olive Tree, an allusion to the form of the leaves of the first species named.

Paractaenum novaehollandiae A.M.F.J.P. de Beauvois (1812) Poaceae
Reflexed Panic Grass

Dampier's specimen remained unnamed until 1938 when Charles Hubbard and Charles Gardner recognised it as this species.

Palisot de Beauvois described the genus in 1812, based on an unknown collection from Australia. The generic name is derived from the Greek words *para* (beside, alongside) and *cteis*, *ctenos* (a comb), and presumably refers to the bristly bracts beside the spikelets. The epithet reflects the name of the continent as known at that time.

This is a slender, ephemeral grass with short racemes of spikelets that bend downwards as they mature. It occurs only in Australia but is widespread in all States except Victoria and Tasmania, commonly growing on sand dunes. It is the only species of its genus.

Pittosporum phylliraeoides A.P. de Candolle (1824) Pittosporaceae
Native Willow

Dampier's specimens were not studied by Ray or Plukenet. The genus was named in 1788 by the German botanist Joseph Gaertner. The name is derived from the Greek *pitta* (pitch) and *sporos* (seed), in reference to the sticky gum that surrounds the seeds.

The species was named from a specimen collected by Leschenault on the Baudin voyage, probably from Shark Bay in 1801. The epithet is derived from the resemblance of the leaves to those of *Phillyrea angustifolia*, a Mediterranean shrub of the olive family (its generic name has had several spellings).

As currently known, this is a variable species. In Western Australia there are two forms, an erect, small bushy tree mainly of coastal areas from Shark Bay south to Perth; the type specimen and Dampier's plant represent this form. Inland, and extending through much of temperate and arid Australia, is a taller form with long, slender, pendulous branchlets; this is known as var. *microcarpa*.

Sida calyxhymenia J.E. Gay ex A.P. de Candolle (1824) Malvaceae

Ray described this as '*Alcea* Novæ Hollandiæ' with narrow leaves villous on both sides. 'In the middle stands a Columella thick set with thrummy apiculae, which argue this Plant to belong to the Malvaceous kind'. He was correct in this assessment. The 'thrummy apiculae' — which loosely means short threads with tips — are the stamens. *Alcea* is the genus to which hollyhocks belong, hence the association with this plant is correct. Dampier's figure matches the specimen well.

The genus *Sida* was named by Carl Linnaeus in 1753. The name is thought to be derived from the Greek *side* (a pomegranate or waterlily), but the reason for the association of this word with the hibiscus family is obscure. John Gay described the species from a collection by Leschenault, probably from Shark Bay and not from the Swan River as stated by I.D. Clement in 1957, as there are no other collections from the Swan River. His epithet is based on the Greek *calyx* (a cup, hence the calyx of a flower) and *hymen* (a skin or membrane), in reference to the thinly textured calyx of the plant. He did not publish the name directly, but it was taken up and published by Augustin de Candolle.

This is a rather slender, closely hairy shrub growing to 1.5 metres tall, widespread in arid and semi-arid regions of Western and Central Australia.

Solanum orbiculatum M.F. Dunal ex J.L.M. Poiret (1814) Solanaceae
Wild Tomato

Ray described this as 'Solanum spinosum Novæ Hollandiæ, Phylli foliis subrotundis', i.e. A spinose Solanum of New Holland, [?] with almost round leaves. Since 'phyllum' is the Greek for leaf and 'folium' is the Latin, the reason for the inclusion of 'Phylli' here is not clear, especially since 'i' is not a normal ending for this word. The name Solanum was already well established in Dampier's day for other plants in this cosmopolitan genus, hence Ray would have readily recognised the affinity of this plant. Linnaeus confirmed its use in modern nomenclature in 1753.

The later naming of the species was entirely a French affair. Michel Dunal (a botanist at Montpellier) described it from specimens gathered at Shark Bay, either in winter 1801 or autumn 1803, by one of the collectors on the French voyage of discovery led by Thomas Nicholas Baudin. The epithet *orbiculatum* clearly refers to the leaf shape. The plant is a shrub to 1.5 metres tall, covered with velvety, stellate hairs, with a purple corolla about 2 centimetres wide. It is widespread from the central west coast of Western Australia through the arid interior to the southern Northern Territory and western South Australia. Although Dampier's specimens are in flower only, it is very likely that the plants also had their spherical fruit at the time of his visit and were one of the 'berries' that he referred to during his visit to Dirk Hartog Island.

His figure matches the right-hand specimen (reversed).

Thryptomene baeckeacea F. Mueller (1864) Myrtaceae

This is the plant described by Plukenet in 1705 as 'Erica *Nov'hollandica* quaterno ordine foliata, folio subrotundo brevi', i.e. an Erica of New Holland with leaves in four rows, the leaf almost round, short. Figure 4 of plate 451 is the same plant, even though it is there labelled as being from Amboina; 'Pl. 11' in the caption refers to the text account just quoted. The figure, which approximates one of Dampier's specimens, was interpreted by Osborn and Gardner (1939) as *Beaufortia dampieri*, and by George (1971) as *Melaleuca cardiophylla*, but in fact represents *Thryptomene baeckeacea*.

The genus *Thryptomene* was named in 1838 by the German botanist Stephan Endlicher, using the Greek word *thryptomene* meaning diminished, presumably in reference to the small flowers. Thryptomenes occur only in Australia, with over 30 species now known.

Mueller's type collection of this species was gathered by Augustus Oldfield near Oakajee, between Geraldton and the lower Murchison River. The specific epithet reflects the resemblance of the plant to species of the related genus *Baeckea*.

This is another shrub with very small leaves that may have reminded Dampier of the heaths in England, as he remarked while at Dirk Hartog Island in 1699. The tiny pink flowers form a quite attractive display in late winter and early spring. The species occurs on the mainland around Shark Bay and north as far as Coral Bay, with a long-leaved variant in the Cape Range.

Trachymene elachocarpa (F. Mueller) B.L. Burtt (1941) Apiaceae

Plukenet described this as 'Umbelliferis adfinis, Ranunculi folio, planta pusilla *Hollandiæ Novæ*', i.e. Resembling Umbelliferae, with the leaf of a Ranunculus, a very small plant of New Holland. His interpretation was correct, as this plant does belong to the family Umbelliferae (now usually called Apiaceae), and the leaves do resemble those of many species of *Ranunculus*. He did not illustrate it.

The first modern name of the species was *Didiscus elachocarpus*, published by Mueller in 1892, and based on a specimen that he collected between the lower Murchison River and Shark Bay in 1877. *Didiscus* is a genus very similar to *Trachymene*, and a number of Australian species were named under it before being transferred to the latter genus. The epithet was derived from the Greek *elachys* (small, short) and *carpos* (a fruit). The plant is a small, stiffly hairy annual herb that was quite common on Bernier Island at the time of our visit in August 1998. I saw none during our short time ashore on Dirk Hartog Island but recorded it there in 1971. Dampier's specimens, somewhat damaged by insects, are of similar size to those that I saw, indicating a similar season.

The generic name *Trachymene* was published in 1811 by Edward Rudge, an English botanist. The name is derived from the Greek *trachys* (rough) and *hymen* (skin), in reference to the surface of the fruit of the type species (sometimes given as from *mene* (the moon), as each half of the fruit is half-moon shaped).

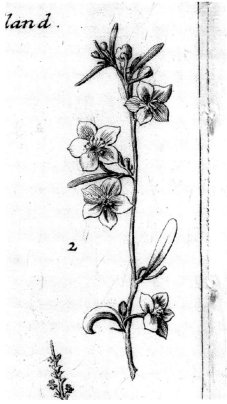

Sida calyxhmenia. Left, Dampier's specimen. Right, figure from his *Voyage to New Holland*, Tab. 3, fig. 2.

Photo: A.S. George

Sida calyxhmenia, plant (left), flower (right).

Photos: A.S. George

Solanum orbiculatum.

Left, Dampier's specimens.

The labels are: upper left,

Charles Gardner, 1938; middle left,

Hermia Newman Clokie, c.1960;

lower left, unknown;

upper right, Humphrey Sibthorp,

between 1747 and 1783;

lower right, William Sherard,

early 18th century.

Photograph courtesy of the Department of Plant Sciences, University of Oxford

Solanum orbiculatum, shrub (left), flower and foliage (right).

Photos: A.S. George

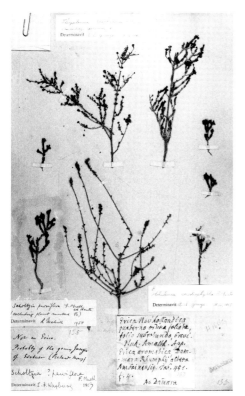
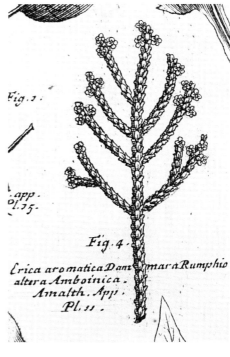

Thryptomene baeckeacea. Left, Dampier's specimens (mixed with *Melaleuca* — the specimen marked 'B').

The labels are: top, A.S. George, 1968; upper left, Ronald Melville, 1958; centre left, unknown;

bottom left, E.F. Warburg, 1957; upper right, A.S. George, 1968; lower right, William Sherard, early 18th century.

Right, figure from Plukenet, *Amaltheum Botanicum*, Plate 452, fig. 4.

Photo: A.S. George

Thryptomene baeckeacea, plant (left), flowers and foliage (right).

Photos: A.S. George

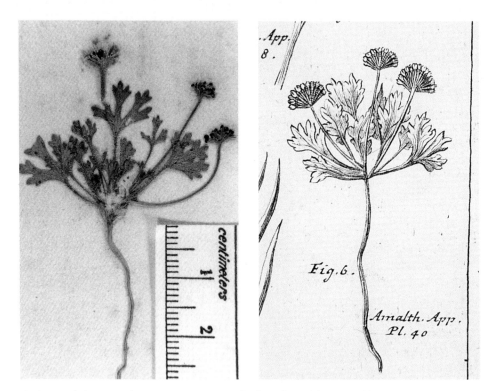

Trachymene elachocarpa. Left, Dampier's specimen. Right, figure from Plukenet, *Amaltheum Botanicum*, Plate 454, fig. 6.

Photo: A.S. George

Trachymene elachocarpa, plants in flower and fruit.

Photo: A.S. George

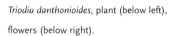

Triodia danthonioides. Dampier's specimen.

Photo: A.S. George

Triodia danthonioides, plant (below left),

flowers (below right).

Photos: A.S. George

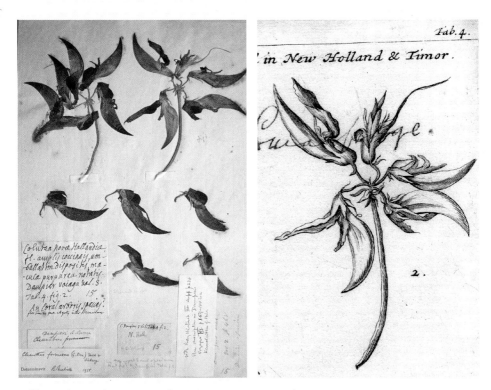

Willdampia formosa, the Sturt Pea. Left, Dampier's specimens; see also page 36.

Right, figure from his *Voyage to New Holland*, Tab. 4, fig. 2.

Photo: A.S. George

Willdampia formosa on East Lewis Island.

Photo: K.F. Kenneally

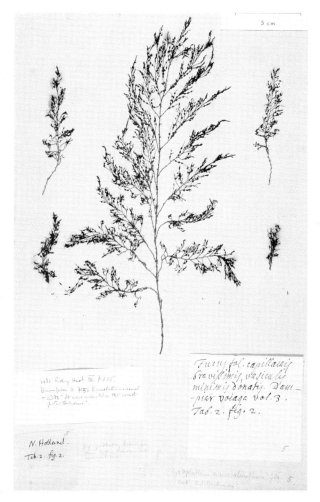

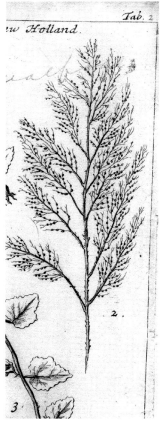

Cystoseira trinodis. Above, Dampier's specimen. The labels are:

upper left, Hermia Newman Clokie, c.1960;

lower left, Humphrey Sibthorp, between 1747 and 1783;

lower centre (written directly on the sheet), unknown;

upper right, William Sherard, early 18th century;

lower right, Carola I. Dickinson, 1950s.

Above right, figure from his *Voyage to New Holland*, Tab. 2, fig. 2.

Photo courtesy of the Department of Plant Sciences, University of Oxford

Cystoseira trinodis, in situ on ocean floor.

Photo: J. Huisman

Abrus precatorius subsp. *precatorius*, Crabs Eyes: flowers and foliage.

Photo: A.S. George

Abrus precatorius subsp.
precatorius, Crabs Eyes: open pods
with seeds.

Photo: B.J. Carter

Acanthocarpus robustus. Figure from Plukenet, *Amaltheum Botanicum*, Plate 451, fig. 9.

Acanthocarpus robustus, plant (above), fruit and foliage (right).

Photos: A.S. George

Jack Bean, *Canavalia rosea*, plant (above),
flowers (below left), pod (right).

Photos: A.S. George

Green Birdflower, *Crotalaria cunninghamii*,
plant (above), flowers and foliage (right).

Photos: A.S. George

Beach Morning Glory, *Ipomoea
pes-caprae* subsp. *brasiliensis*,
flower and foliage.

Photo: A.S. George

Nitre Bush, *Nitraria billardierei*, flowers and foliage.

Ptilotus villosiflorus. Figure from Plukenet, *Amaltheum Botanicum*, Plate 441, fig. 5.

A mulla mulla, *Ptilotus villosiflorus*, plant in flower.

Beach Spinifex, *Spinifex longifolius*, male (left) and female plants with flowers (right).

Photos: A.S. George

Sand Hibiscus, *Alyogyne pinoniana*; plant (above), flower and foliage (right).

Photos: A.S. George

Climbing Daisy, *Brachycome latisquamea*; plant (left), flowers (right).

Photos: A.S. George

Halgania littoralis; foliage and flowers.

Photo: A.S. George

Scaevola crassifolia; foliage and flowers.

Photo: A.S. George

Scaevola holosericea; plant (above),
foliage and flowers (right).

Photos: A.S. George

Solanum lasiophyllum; shrub, flowers.

Photo: A.S. George

Camel Bush, *Trichodesma zeylanicum*; flowers.

Photo: A.S. George

Triodia danthonioides (F. Mueller) M. Lazarides (1997) Poaceae
Triraphis danthonioides F. Mueller (1873);
Plectrachne danthonioides (F. Mueller) C.E. Hubbard (1939)
Spinifex

Dampier's specimen is a flowering stem only. Either he decided that the leaves were too sharp to collect, or the leaves have been lost. The specimen was not studied closely until the 1930s, when Charles Hubbard, at the Royal Botanic Gardens, Kew, recognised it as a species of *Plectrachne*, later placing it in *P. danthonioides*. This name was used until 1997.

The genus *Triodia* was named in 1810 by Robert Brown, who derived the name from the Greek *tri-* (three-) and *odous* (a tooth), the lemma of the flower being three-toothed. The original specimen used by Ferdinand Mueller to name the species in 1873 was collected at an unknown locality in south-western Australia by James Drummond. He did not recognise it as a *Triodia* but placed it in the genus *Triraphis*. His epithet refers to the resemblance of the inflorescence to that of another grass genus, *Danthonia*. During Hubbard's research into grasses he realised that Mueller's species belonged to *Plectrachne* as then accepted and transferred it to that genus. For many years the 'soft' spinifexes with long-awned lemmas were placed in *Plectrachne*, but following a revision of all species of this genus and *Triodia*, Michael Lazarides concluded that there are insufficient morphological grounds for keeping them separate and in 1997 transferred all species of *Plectrachne* to *Triodia*, the earlier generic name (Lazarides, 1997).

Triodia contains the needle-leaved tufted grasses known as spinifex that are so common through the arid and semi-arid regions of Australia. *Triodia danthonioides* is locally common in Western Australia between Shark Bay and the Hill River, mainly in near-coastal situations. It grows in sandy soil in clumps to 2 metres across, with flowering stems to 1.5 metres tall.

Willdampia formosa (G. Don) A.S. George (1999) Fabaceae
Sturt Pea

This was listed as *Clianthus dampieri* by Mueller (1883), as *Clianthus speciosus* by Osborn and Gardner (1939), and as *Clianthus formosus* by George (1971) and other recent authors except Gill (1997). Since 1990 it has also been known as *Swainsona formosa*. All names are synonyms of *Willdampia formosa*.

It is fitting that this spectacular plant should finally bear a formal name commemorating its discoverer. John Ray called it 'Colutea Novæ Hollandiæ, floribus amplis coccineis, umbellatim dispositis, macula purpurea notatis', i.e. a *Colutea* of New Holland, with large scarlet flowers, arranged in an umbel, marked with a purple spot. *Colutea* is a name now used for a genus of peas found from the Mediterranean to China and north-eastern Africa. Ray was somehat doubtful, however, adding that it might be a species of coral tree [*Erythrina*] since the flowers were similar — he apparently did not see Dampier's description of it as a creeping vine.

Under the Linnaean naming system the plant first received the name *Donia formosa* G. Don in 1832, based on specimens collected at the Curlew [now Ashburton] River, Western Australia, on 20 February 1818, apparently by Frederick Bedwell, master of HMC *Mermaid* in which Phillip Parker King made his first circumnavigation surveying the Australian coast. From 1950 it was known as *Clianthus formosus* (G. Don) Ford & Vickery. Although widely accepted that it should not be included in this genus (the first-named *Clianthus* being a New Zealand plant that differs in significant features), no-one took the step to remove it until 1990 when Joy Thompson transferred it to *Swainsona* during her study of that genus (Thompson, 1990). Because I believe that it is sufficiently different from all other swainsonas to warrant its own genus, I have recently published the name *Willdampia* for it (George, 1999).

The epithet *formosa* (handsome, beautiful) refers to the flowers. Dampier's figure matches the upper right-hand specimen on the herbarium sheet.

Cystoseira trinodis (P. Forsskål) C. Agardh 1820 Cystoseiraceae

In early August 1699, as the *Roebuck* was approaching the Western Australian coast, the crew began to observe objects floating in the sea, including 'Sea-weeds, all of one sort'. Just when Dampier gathered a specimen and dried it is unknown; he simply stated that it was 'collected on the Coast of New Holland'. They must have scooped up floating material since Dampier also described curious spheres (see p. 107), so the seaweed may have been among this; but it could also have been picked up on the beach during one of the landings. It is the first specimen of a seaweed collected in Australia and is housed with his other specimens in the Fielding–Druce Herbarium at Oxford (Ducker, 1990). In his *Voyage* (1703) he illustrated it in Tabula 2, figure 2, with the description '*Fucus foliis capillaceis brevissimis, vesiculis minimis donatis*'. As in many of his accounts, it was compared with seaweeds seen elsewhere — 'This elegant fucus is of the *Erica Marina* or *Sargazo* kind, but has much finer parts than that' — a translation of that in Latin by John Ray (1704, p. 225).

The seaweed is *Cystoseira trinodis* (P. Forsskål) C. Agardh, one of the brown algae (Phaeophyta). It was originally named *Fucus trinodis* in 1775 by Pehr Forsskål based on a specimen collected near El Tür on the Sinai coast of the Red Sea, and transferred to the genus *Cystoseira* by Carl Adolph Agardh in 1820. The generic name is formed from the Greek *cysto-* (a bladder or sac) and *seira* (a chain or rope), in reference to the strings of vesicles formed along the branches; and the species name refers to the vesicles (usually in groups of three) that occur on the branchlets. In 1848 the species was placed in the genus *Cystophyllum* by J.G. Agardh but that change has not been accepted by other phycologists. In the 1950s, C.I. Dickinson determined Dampier's specimen as *Cystophyllum muricatum* (C. Agardh) J.G. Agardh, a name accepted for the species at the time but now placed in synonymy. The species is widespread in tropical and subtropical seas of the Indian Ocean, around Indonesia, and around the Australian coast except in Victoria and Tasmania. It is a rather slender plant to 1.5 metres high when growing in sheltered waters such as estuaries but is more robust and shorter in oceanic habitats. The floating mats that accumulate off the coast are probably winter storm drift (Roberta Cowan, pers. comm.).

Other plants seen by Dampier but not represented by specimens

The following plants can be identified from Dampier's journal, in part from his description, in part from data on the distribution and habitat of the species. I have also included *Acanthocarpus robustus* since the diagnosis and figure (plate 451, figure 9) in Plukenet appear to be this species, and *Ptilotus villosiflorus* which seems to be represented in plate 441, figure 5.

Abrus precatorius C. Linnaeus subsp. *precatorius* (1767) Fabaceae (p. 84)
A common tropical climber, with toxic seeds. Seen by Dampier at Lagrange Bay.

Acanthocarpus robustus A.S. George (1986) Xanthorrhoeaceae (p. 85)
A tough, clumped, grass-like plant with small white flowers and round fruit covered with hard tubercles, occurring from Shark Bay to North West Cape. As discussed above, this was not previously recognised as one of Dampier's Australian plants; it was probably collected on Dirk Hartog Island but is not among the extant specimens.

Canavalia rosea (O. Swartz) A.P. de Candolle (1825) Fabaceae (p. 86)
Originally named *Dolichos roseus* by Swartz in 1788. Given as *Canavalia obtusifolia* by Mueller (1883) and George (1971). A common beach plant in tropical countries. Probably seen by Dampier on East Lewis Island and at Lagrange Bay.

Crotalaria cunninghamii R. Brown (1849) Fabaceae (p. 87)
A common sand dune shrub of the north-west coast, the Kimberley and the deserts. Seen by Dampier on East Lewis Island and at Lagrange Bay.

Ipomoea pes-caprae (C. Linnaeus) R. Brown (1818) subsp. *brasiliensis* (C. Linnaeus) S.J. van Ooststroom (1940) Convolvulaceae (p. 87)
Both the specific and subspecific epithets were first published as species of *Convolvulus* in 1753 by Linnaeus. A common beach plant of tropical countries. Probably seen by Dampier on East Lewis Island and possibly at Lagrange Bay.

Nitraria billardierei A.P. de Candolle (1828) Zygophyllaceae (p. 88)

A common, succulent-leaved shrub of the southern Australian coast. Seen by Dampier on Dirk Hartog Island and likened to the European samphire, *Crithmum*. For many years known as *Nitraria schoberi* C. Linnaeus. See also pp. 9, 10.

Ptilotus villosiflorus F. Mueller (1862) Amaranthaceae (p. 88)

A small, soft-leaved ephemeral herb with woolly pink and white flowers, common in near-coastal parts of the central west coast of Western Australia. As discussed above, this was not previously recognised as one of Dampier's Australian plants; it was probably collected on Dirk Hartog Island but is not among the extant specimens.

Spinifex longifolius R. Brown (1810) Poaceae (p. 89)

A common coastal dune grass of southern Australia. Seen by Dampier on Dirk Hartog Island.

✳

Other blue flowers probably seen by Dampier but not among the specimens or mentioned in his journal

When he landed on Dirk Hartog Island, Dampier was impressed by the number of plants with blue flowers. Only three of his specimens have blue or mauve flowers (*Dampiera incana*, *Brachycome* aff. *cheilocarpa*, *Solanum orbiculatum*), but others grow in the area that he would have explored. Of those illustrated below, the *Halgania*, *Brachycome* and two species of *Scaevola* are common and conspicuous in the vegetation near Dampier Landing.

Alyogyne pinoniana (C. Gaudichaud-Beaupré) P.A. Fryxell (1968) Malvaceae (p. 89)

Originally named *Hibiscus pinonianus* by Gaudichaud-Beaupré in 1826. A common shrub in north-western and arid Australia.

Brachycome latisquamea F. Mueller (1878) Asteraceae (p. 90)

A perennial scrambling plant endemic in the Shark Bay area.

Halgania littoralis C. Gaudichaud-Beaupré (1829) Boraginaceae (p. 90)
A small shrub of the area from Shark Bay to Geraldton, conspicuous in the
vegetation near Dampier Landing on Dirk Hartog Island.

Scaevola crassifolia J.J.H. de Labillardière (1805) Goodeniaceae (p. 91)
A common coastal shrub in south-western Australia, growing as far north as
North West Cape, conspicuous in the vegetation near Dampier Landing on
Dirk Hartog Island.

Scaevola holosericea W.H. de Vriese (1845) Goodeniaceae (p. 91)
A conspicuous perennial herb in the vegetation near Dampier Landing on
Dirk Hartog Island.

Solanum lasiophyllum M.F. Dunal ex J.L.M. Poiret (1814) Solanaceae (p. 92)
A closely woolly but also prickly shrub very widespread in arid and
semi-arid Australia.

Trichodesma zeylanicum (N.L. Burman f.) R. Brown (1810)
Boraginaceae (p. 92)
Originally named *Borago zeylanica* by Burman in 1768. Probably seen also on
East Lewis Island and at Lagrange Bay. A perennial herb common in northern
Australia, islands to the north, south-east Asia and India.

It is possible that Dampier also saw the blue-flowered *Porana sericea*
(C. Gaudichaud-Beaupré) F. Mueller (1868), a member of the Convolvulaceae
(George, 1971). Originally named *Duperreya sericea* by Gaudichaud-Beaupré in
1828, this is a small climber endemic in the area from Ajana to Gnaraloo and
inland to Meekatharra. It has been recorded from Dirk Hartog Island.
I was unable to obtain a photograph for the book.

Dampier's Australian animals

Birds

SERVENTY AND WHITTELL (1962) reviewed the birds recorded by Dampier and other early voyagers. From 1618 onwards, Dutch seamen had mentioned some species in letters and journals. Francisco Pelsaert, who was wrecked on the Abrolhos Islands in 1629, mentioned birds in the published account of his experiences. In 1697, Willem de Vlamingh described the black swan for the first time, also mentioning a number of other species and describing the footprint of an emu. On his visit in 1688, Dampier made no record of birds, but on his second visit he noted many species, giving more detail than previous observers. In his account of the voyage he published the first illustrations of Australian birds, drawn by a member of his crew. By modern standards the drawings are rather crude but yet are recognisable.

On 7 August 1699, approaching the west coast of new Holland, Damper wrote:

> the Birds that had flown along with us all the way almost from Brazil, now left us, except 2 or 3 Shear-waters.

Among these may have been Cape Petrels (*Daption capense* Linnaeus, 1758) which were illustrated by Dampier in Figure 1 of *Voyage to New Holland*. He wrote: 'We saw these Birds, especially the Pintado-birds, all the Sea over from about 200 Leagues distant from the coast of Brazil, to within much the same distance of *New Holland*'. He then described three kinds of pintado but said that the 'true Pintado is curiously spotted white and black ... We shot one a while after in a Calm, and a Water-Spaniel we had with us brought it in; I have given a Picture of it [See *Birds*, Fig. 1.]'. This, the Cape Petrel with a wingspan of 80–90 centimetres, generally remains far out at sea but occasionally is seen in winter along southern Australian shores. It was included in the plate with the four New Holland birds in a French broadsheet published soon after his book appeared (L.R. Marchant, 1988, p. 2).

Three days later, on 10 August, as they were sailing up the coast off the Zuytdorp Cliffs, Dampier wrote:

> [we] saw also a sort of Fowls the like of which we had not seen in the whole Voyage, all the other Fowls having now left us. These were as big as Lapwings; of a grey Colour, black about their Eyes, with red sharp Bills, long Wings, their Tails long and forked like Swallows; and they flew flapping their Wings like Lapwings ... The Birds last mentioned were further Signs of Land.

This is the Caspian Tern, *Sterna caspia* Pallas, 1770. It is one of the largest terns, distributed widely in North America, Europe, Africa and through Asia to Australia and New Zealand. Given this wide range, it is perhaps surprising that Dampier seems not to have seen it eslewhere.

On 12 August they were approaching the southern end of Dirk Hartog Island and saw an opening in the coast (South Passage) where they thought an entry might be possible. Dampier wrote:

This Morning, ... as we were standing in we saw several large Sea-fowls, like our Gannets on the Coast of *England*, flying three or four together; and a sort of white Sea-Mews, but black about the Eyes, and with forked Tails.

The first of these is the Australian Gannet, *Sula serrator* (G.R. Gray, 1843), and the second probably the Crested Tern, *Sterna bergii* Lichtenstein, 1823. This Gannet occurs only in Australia, mainly around the southern coast. Shark Bay is almost its northern limit on the west coast. The Crested Tern occurs around the Indian Ocean and through Southeast Asia as far north as Japan. It is common around the whole Australian coast.

From 16 to 21 August the *Roebuck* was at anchor off Dampier Landing, Dirk Hartog Island. Dampier landed several times, and summed up the bird life thus:

There were but few Land-Fowls: we saw none but Eagles, of the larger sorts of Birds, but 5 or 6 sorts of small Birds. The biggest sort of these were not bigger than Larks; some no bigger than Wrens, all singing with great variety of fine shrill Notes; and we saw some of their Nests with young Ones in them. The Water-Fowls are Ducks (which had young Ones now, this being the Beginning of the Spring in these Parts;) Curlews, Galdens, Crab-catchers, Cormorants, Gulls, Pelicans; and some Water-Fowl, such as I have not seen any where besides. I have given the Pictures of several Birds on this Coast [See *Birds*: Fig. 2, 3, 4, 5.].

The cormorant is the Pied Cormorant, *Phalacrocorax varius* (Gmelin, 1789). Galden was Dampier's name for a species of heron — the Eastern

Reef Heron (*Egretta sacra* Gmelin, 1789) has been recorded for the island (Burbidge & George, 1978). His 'crab-catcher' is the Pied Oystercatcher, *Haematopus longirostris* Vieillot, 1817, illustrated as Figure 4 in his account of the voyage, and the pelican is the Australian pelican, *Pelecanus conspicillatus* Temminck, 1824. Dampier would have been familiar with oystercatchers in Europe and pelicans in the West Indies. The eagle cannot be identified with certainty as several species are known there, including the Wedge-tailed Eagle, *Aquila audax* (Latham, 1802), White-bellied Sea Eagle, *Haliaeetus leucogaster* (Gmelin, 1788) and the eagle-like Osprey, *Pandion haliaetus* (Linnaeus, 1758). Two gulls occur on Dirk Hartog Island — the Silver Gull, *Larus novaehollandiae* Stephens, 1826, and the Pacific Gull, *Larus pacificus* Latham, 1802. The former is found around the whole Australian coast as well as in New Zealand and southern Africa, but the latter is found only in Australia. Likewise, several ducks are known there — the one most likely to have been seen by Dampier is the Grey Teal, *Anas gibberfrons* Buller, 1869.

Dampier's account of small birds singing with great variety of shrill notes is his only mention of bird song. Several very melodious species are common on the island, including the Black-and-white Fairy-wren (*Malurus leucopterus leucopterus* Dumont, 1824) which is endemic there, the Singing Honeyeater (*Meliphaga virescens* Vieillot, 1817) and Richard's Pipit (*Anthus novaeseelandiae australis* Vieillot, 1818).

The numbering in Dampier's plate (Figures 3–6) is at odds with his text reference 'See *Birds*: Fig. 2, 3, 4, 5'.

In Figure 3 of his *Voyage to New Holland*, Dampier showed the Red-necked Avocet, *Recurvirostra novaehollandiae* Vieillot, 1816, though there is no mention of it in the text, hence we do not know where he saw it. A wading bird, it feeds on minute crustaceans in shallow water and occurs throughout Australia.

On 3 September, Dampier landed on East Lewis Island in the Dampier Archipelago.

We saw here some Cormorants, Gulls, Crabcatchers, &c. a few small Land Birds, and a sort of white Parrots, which flew a great many together.

The parrots would have been the Little Corella, *Cacatua sanguinea* Gould (1843). These move in flocks and can be very noisy when calling. They are common in north-western Australia, the Kimberley, throughout the Northern Territory and drier parts of the other States. The other birds seen here are discussed above.

After negotiating the Dampier Archipelago, Dampier stood farther off the coast as he sailed north-east. On 7 September, they were well out to sea, and Dampier wrote:

We saw also some *Boobies*, and Noddy-birds; and in the Night caught one of these last. It was of another Shape and Colour than any I had seen before. It had a small long Bill, as all of them have, flat Feet like Ducks Feet; its Tail forked like a Swallow, but longer and broader, and the Fork deeper than that of the Swallow, with very long Wings; The Top or Crown of the Head of this Noddy was Coal-black, having also small black Streaks round about and close to the Eyes; and round these Streaks on each side, a pretty broad white Circle. The Breast, Belly, and under part of the Wings of this Noddy were white: And the Back and upper part of its Wings of a faint black or smoak Colour. See a Picture of this, and of the Common one, *Birds*, Fig. 5, 6. Noddies are seen in most Places between the *Tropicks*, as well as in the *East-Indies*, and on the Coast of *Brazil*, as in the *West-Indies*. They rest a Shore a Nights, and therefore we never see them far at Sea, not above 20 or 30 Leagues, unless driven off in a Storm. When they come about a Ship they commonly perch in the Night, and will sit still till they are taken by the Seamen. They Build on Cliffs against the Sea, or Rocks, as I have said in Vol. I. p. 53.

Two species of booby occur in the area — the Masked Booby, *Sula dactylatra* Lesson, 1831, and the Brown Booby, *Sula leucogaster* Boddaert, 1783. Both are widespread in tropical and subtropical oceans and would have been familiar to Dampier. The 'noddy' described here by him in detail and illustrated in his Figure 5 is the Bridled Tern, *Sterna anaethetus* Scopoli, 1786, common around the west and north coasts of Australia and in all tropical seas. His Figure 6 shows a Common Noddy, *Anous stolidus* (Linnaeus, 1758), a widespread oceanic bird but less common in cooler regions. In northern Australia it is seen from the north-west coast to the Great Barrier Reef.

They headed towards the coast again, and by 9 September were anchored in Lagrange Bay where once more they landed, seeking much-needed fresh water. Here Dampier made further observations on the natural history:

> The Land-fowls that we saw here were Crows (just such as ours in *England*) small Hawks, and Kites; a few of each sort: but here are plenty of small Turtle-Doves, that are plump, fat and very good Meat. Here are 2 or 3 smaller Birds, some as big as Larks, some less; but not many of either sort. The Sea-Fowl are Pelicans, Boobies, Noddies, Curlews, Sea-pies, &c. and but few of these neither.

Two species of crow occur in the region-the Torresian Crow, *Corvus orru* Bonaparte, 1852, and the Little Crow, *Corvus bennettii* North, 1912. The former is common in Australia except in southern regions and extends to New Guinea and other islands of the south-western Pacific Ocean. The Little Crow is endemic and common in the drier parts of all mainland States. It is not possible to identify the hawks and kites as a number of species occur here. The turtle doves were possibly the Peaceful Dove, *Geopelia striata* (Linnaeus, 1766), a species widespread in northern and eastern Australia and through the islands to the north. 'Sea-pie' is Dampier's name for a wader. The other species are discussed above.

Having failed to find water, Dampier decided to head for Timor and so left the Australian coast, passing well out to sea from his landing site of 1688. On 20 September they sailed, near 'a small low sandy Island', probably Browse Island in the Timor Sea off the Kimberley coast, where:

> We had Abundance of Boobies and Man of War Birds flying about us all the Day; especially when we came near the Island; which had also Abundance of them upon it; though it was but a little Spot of Sand, scarce a Mile around.

The Man of War is probably the Lesser Frigatebird, *Fregata ariel* (G.R. Gray, 1845). The boobies are discussed above.

✳

Sea life

Eight Australian species of marine animals were illustrated in plates 1, 2 and 3, between pages 124 and 125, of Dampier's *Voyage to New Holland* (1703) — as with the other figures, these are the first of Australian marine animals. The drawings, by his draughtsman, tend to be less accurate than the others and, as discussed below, cannot all be identified to species or even genus. The only mention by Dampier of scientific reference works is in his discussion of fishes: *Ichthyographia* (1685) and *Historia Piscium* (1686) by Francis Willughby (1635–1672) and one by Willem Piso (1611–1678), probably his *De Indiae* etc. of 1658. Dampier's plates are interpreted below and reproduced on pages 113 (Plate 1), 115 (Plate 2) and 116 (Plate 3).

Plate 1, figure 1. This is likely to be a flathead of the family Platycephalidae as these have a long snout as shown in the figure. Other possibilities are Opisthognathidae (jawfish) or Batrachoididae (frogfish). Finney (1984) considered that it might be an angel shark, *Squatina australis*.

Plate 1, figure 3. This is possibly a species of *Malacanthus* (family Malancanthidae), now commonly known as blanquillos or tilefish. Two species occur around northern Australia — the Flagtail Blanquillo, *M. brevirostris* Guichenot, 1848, recorded from Ningaloo Reef northward, and the Blue Blanquillo, *M. latovittatus* (Lacépède, 1801).

Plate 1, figure 6. This is still known as a remora, indeed its scientific name is *Remora remora* (Linnaeus, 1758), family Echeneididae. It occurs in all Australian tropical and temperate waters, usually attached to sharks, rays and other large fish but occasionally found swimming free.

Plate 1, figure 8. Called a 'cuttle' by Dampier and mentioned several times in his journal, this cannot be identified with certainty (see below).

Plate 1, figure 9. Many species of flying fish (family Exocoetidae) occur around the Dampier Archipelago and the drawing cannot be identified to genus or species.

Plate 2, figure 2. This is the common Bottle-nose Dolphin of the north-west coast, *Tursiops truncatus* (Montagu, 1821). Dampier called it a 'Dolphin of the Antients' [Ancients] and said that it was caught 'near ye Line', i.e. the Equator. The dolphin was known to the Romans (Latin, *delphinus*).

Plate 2, figure 7. The Dolphin Fish or Dorado is *Coryphaena hippurus* Linnaeus, 1758.

Plate 3, figure 4. Labelled the Old Wife, this is probably the Queen Triggerfish, *Balistes vetula* Linnaeus, 1758, a species from the Atlantic Ocean and mistakenly included here by Dampier. He may have confused it with the Starry Triggerfish *Abalistes stellatus* Linnaeus, 1758, a species of the north-western Australian coast.

Plate 3, figure 5. This is probably not a tuna as known today but a spanish mackerel, *Scomberomorus commerson* (Lacépède, 1802).

Dampier's first mention of marine life off the western Australian coast was on 4 August when they were near the Abrolhos Islands. They saw:

a large Gar-fish leap four times by us, which seemed to be as big as a Porpose. It was now very fair Weather, and the Sea was full of a sort of very small Grass or Moss, which as it floated in the Water seem'd to have been some Spawn of Fish; and there was among it some small Fry. The next Day the Sea was full of small rounds Things like Pearl, some as big as white Peas; they were very clear and transparent, and upon crushing any of them a Drop of Water would come forth: The Skin that contain'd the Water was so thin that it was but just discernable.

The garfish was probably a long tom or alligator pike, a species of either *Strongylura* or *Tylosurus*, family Belonidae, which scoots across the waves as it swims. The 'Grass or Moss' is likely to have been a blue-green alga, probably a species of *Trichodesmium*, that forms floating mats well offshore at that season. The identity of the spheres is unknown.

On 7 August, while sailing north near the coast, they saw 'some Whales, blowing'. Humpback Whales, *Megaptera novaeangliae* (Borowski, 1781), family Balaenopteridae, are common off the Western Australian coast at this time of the year. They feed on krill and small schooling fish. During the summer they feed in Antarctic waters, migrating in early winter to the North-West Shelf to breed, then returning south in early summer.

A little further north, on 8 August:

We saw this Day a Scutle-bone swim by us, and some of our young Men a Seal, as it should seem by their Description of its Head. I saw also some Boneta's, and some Skipjacks, a Fish about 8 Inches long, broad, and sizable, not much unlike a Roach; which our Seamen call so from their leaping about.

and on 9 August:

> being still nearer the Land, we saw abundance of Scutle-bones and
> Sea-weed, more Tokens that we were not far from it.

Dampier also mentioned 'Scuttle-shells' on 27 August, and illustrated an animal in figure 8 as 'A Cuttle taken near N. Holland'. It is not possible to identify this with certainty as it could be one of several species of cuttle-fish (*Sepia*) or a squid (*Sepioteuthis*). Both cuttlefish and squid have eight arms and two longer tentacles, but Dampier's figure shows only seven arms. He also showed the fin extending around the whole of the mantle, whereas the known species have fins only along the sides. The seal was probably the Australian Sea Lion, *Neophoca cinerea* (Péron, 1816), family Otariidae, which occurs along the west and south coast as far east as Bass Strait. The bonita and skipjack are possibly members of the tuna family Scombridae, although the skipjack could have been a trevally (family Carangidae).

During the stay at Dirk Hartog Island from 16 to 21 August, Dampier made extensive observations on the marine life around him.

> The Sea-fish that we saw here (for here was no River, Land or Pond
> of Fresh Water to be seen) are chiefly Sharks. There are abundance
> of them in this particular Sound, that I therefore give it the Name
> of Shark's Bay. Here are also Skates, Thornbacks, and other Fish of
> the Ray-kind; (one sort especially like the Sea-Devil) and Garfish,
> Boneta's &c. Of Shell-fish we got here Muscles, Periwinkles,
> Limpits, Oysters, both of the Pearl-kind and also Eating-Oysters, as
> well the common Sort as long Oysters; beside Cockles, &c. The
> Shore was lined thick with many sorts of very strange and beautiful
> Shells, for variety of Colour and Shape, most finely spotted with
> Red, Black, or Yellow, &c. such as I have not seen any where but
> at this Place. I brought away a great many of them; but lost all,
> except a very few, and those not of the best.

Cape Petrel, *Daption capense*.
Left, Dampier's figure 1, from his
Voyage to New Holland, facing p. 96.

Photo: C. Burton

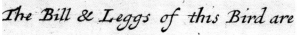

Pied Oystercatcher, *Haematopus longirostris*.
Left, Dampier's figure 4, from his *Voyage to New Holland*, facing p. 123.

Photo: M.K. Morcombe

The head & greatest part of y̆ neck of this bird is red, & therein differs from the Avosetta of Italy.

Red-necked Avocet, *Recurvirostra novaehollandiae*.

Left, Dampier's figure 3, from his *Voyage to New Holland*, facing p. 123.

Photo: M.K. Morcombe

Little Corella,

Cacatua sanguinea.

Photo: M.K. Morcombe

Bridled Tern, *Sterna anaethetus*.
Above, Dampier's figure 5, from his
Voyage to New Holland, facing p. 123.

Photo: M.K. Morcombe

Brown Booby, *Sula leucogaster*, in flight, and a young bird.

Photos: M.K. Morcombe

Common Noddy, *Anous stolidus.*
Dampier's figure 6, from his
Voyage to New Holland, facing p. 123.

Common Noddy, *Anous stolidus.*

Photo: M.K. Morcombe

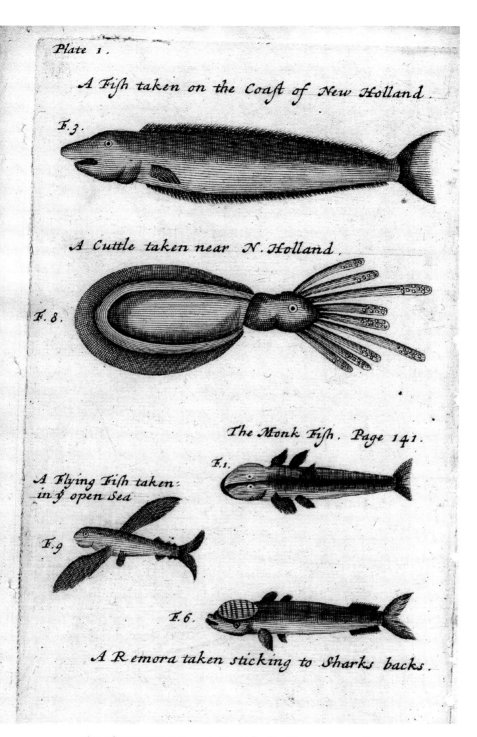

Plate 1.

A Fish taken on the Coast of New Holland.

F.3.

A Cuttle taken near N. Holland.

F. 8.

The Monk Fish. Page 141.

F.1.

A Flying Fish taken in y open Sea

F.9

F.6.

A Remora taken sticking to Sharks backs.

Plate 1 from Dampier's *Voyage to New Holland* (1703); see pp. 105, 106.

A flathead, *Platyaphalus endrachtensis*.

Photo: B. Hutchins

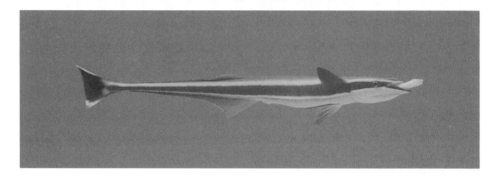

A remora.

Photo: A. Storrie

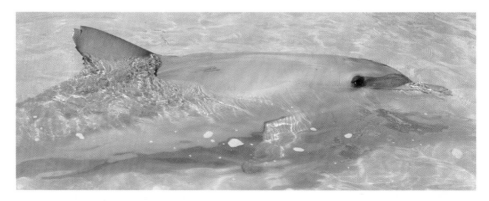

Bottle-nose Dolphin, *Tursiops truncatus*.

Photo: C. Bryce

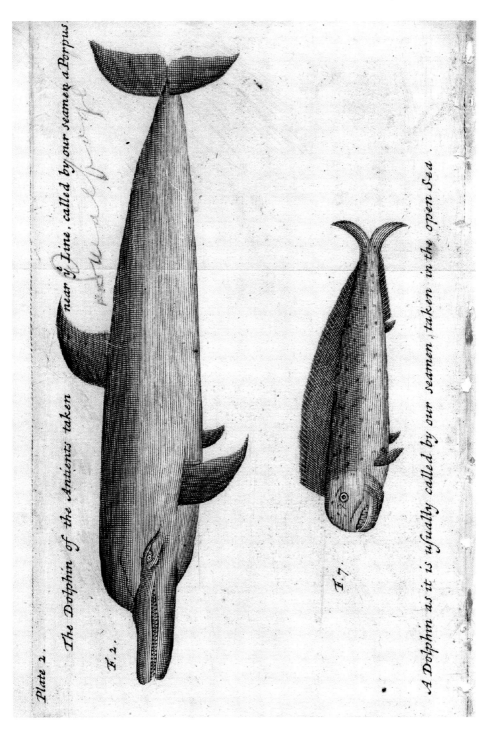

Plate 2 from Dampier's *Voyage to New Holland* (1703); see p. 106.

Plate 3.

A Fish of the Tunny kind taken on y^e Coast of N. Holland

F. 5.

A Fish called by the seamen the Old Wife.

F. 4.

Plate 3 from Dampier's *Voyage to New Holland* (1703); see p. 106.

Above and below left, Humpback Whale, *Megaptera novaeangliae*.

Photos: C. Burton

A cuttlefish, *Sepia* species.

Photo: C. Bryce

An Australian Sea Lion, *Neophoca cinerea*.

Photo: C. Burton

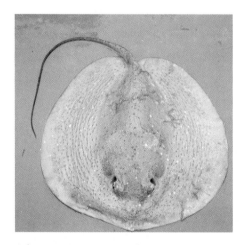

A thorny ray, *Urogymnus asperrimus*.

Photo: B. Hutchins

Rock Oysters at low tide, Dorre Island.

Photo: C. Bryce

The shark-like shovelnose ray *Aptychotrema vincentiana*.

Photo: C. Bryce

Green Turtle, *Chelonia mydas*.

Photo: C. Bryce

A Tiger Shark, *Galeocerdo cuvier.*

Photo: Western Australian Museum

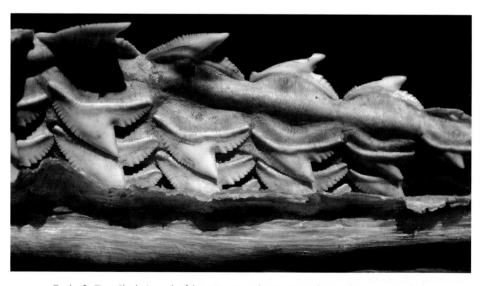

Teeth of a Tiger Shark. As each of those in use on the top row is damaged or worn it is shed, and one from the row below stands up to take its place.

Photo: A.S. George; specimen courtesy of the Western Australian Museum

A Dugong, *Dugong dugon*, with a Slender Suckerfish (below) and a small school of Golden Trevally.

Photo: V. Matson-Larkin

A Potato Cod, *Epinephelus tukula*.

Photo: W. Storrie

An Olive Sea Snake, *Aipysurus laevis*.

Photo: A. Storrie

Shells on the beach at low tide at Lagrange Bay.

Photo: A.S. George

Limpets such as Dampier may have seen on the rocks. The larger are *Patelloida saccharina* (Linnaeus, 1758) and the smaller a species of *Siphonaria*.

Photo: A.S. George

Banded Hare-wallaby, *Lagostrophus fasciatus*.

Photo: M. Lochman

Bush flies, *Musca vetustissima*.

Photo: J. Ridsdill-Smith

Bobtail lizard, *Tiliqua rugosa*, on Dirk Hartog Island.

Photo: A.S. George

The memorial to Dampier in Bedford Park, Broome, with the dedicatory plaque.

Photos: A.S. George

A number of species of shark are known in Shark Bay, hence we cannot determine which they saw. The skate was probably the smooth stingray, *Dasyatis brevicaudata* (Hutton, 1875), family Dasyatididae, a species of southern Australian seas as well as other southern hemisphere countries. Thornbacks may be the thorny ray, *Urogymnus asperrimus* (Bloch and Schneider, 1801), of the same family, widespread in the tropical Indian and Pacific Oceans. Dampier's 'other Fish of the Ray-kind' is likely to have been a shovelnose ray, *Aptychotrema vincentiana* (Haacke, 1885) of the family Rhinobatidae, which is endemic in temperate, inshore waters of Western Australia and South Australia. Garfish, of the family Hemiramphidae, are represented by many species in Shark Bay.

Likewise, there are various species of cockles, mussels, periwinkles and limpets, and Dampier has given no details to allow precise names to be determined for these. The Pearl Oyster is *Pinctada albina* Lamarck, 1818, that, farther north in Western Australia, would later support a valuable industry. It dwells on the seafloor. The 'Eating Oyster' is a species of *Saccostrea* very like *S. commercialis*, the Sydney Rock Oyster. This grows in dense colonies attached to rocks along the tidal zone.

Dampier made quite an extensive collection of seashells but they went down with the *Roebuck* when she foundered off Ascension Island.

There are also some green Turtle, weighing about 200 lb. Of these we caught 2 which the Water Ebbing had left behind a Ledge of Rock, which they could not creep over. These served all my Company 2 days; and they were indifferent sweet Meat.

Green Turtle is still the common name for this turtle which lives in all tropical oceans, sometimes moving into temperate waters. Its scientific name is *Chelonia mydas* (Linnaeus, 1758), family Cheloniidae. Along the north-west coast they lay their eggs on beaches at night, from late October to February. Juveniles feed on various small marine fauna, seaweeds and seagrasses, but adults eat mainly marine plants, including roots.

Of the Sharks we caught a great many, which our Men eat very savourily. Among them we caught one which was 11 Foot long. The space between its 2 Eyes was 20 Inches, and 18 Inches from one Corner of his Mouth to the other. Its Maw was like a Leather Sack, very thick, and so tough that a sharp Knife should scarce cut it: In which we found the Head and Boans of a *Hippopotomus*; the hairy Lips of which were still sound and not putrified, and the Jaw was also firm, out of which we pluckt a great many Teeth, 2 of them 8 Inches long, and as big as a Mans Thumb, small at one End, and a little crooked; the rest not above half so long. The Maw was full of Jelly, which stank extreamly: However I saved for a while the Teeth and the Sharks Jaw.

This shark may have been a Tiger Shark, *Galeocerdo cuvier* (Pron & Lesueur, 1822), family Carcharhinidae, as they prey upon Dugong (the head of which Dampier described as a Hippopotamus!). Tiger Sharks occur in all tropical and temperate oceans but usually stay close to the coast. Dampier kept the jaws of their specimen, but their whereabouts are now unknown. Dugong (*Dugong dugon* (Müller, 1776), family Dugongidae, are a common mammal on tropical Australian coasts but Dampier did not mention seeing live animals. In this case he seems to have forgotten that he saw these (recorded as the 'manatee') during his visit to New Holland in 1688.

On 24 August as they sailed out to sea between Dirk Hartog Island and Dorre Island, Dampier noted sea snakes for the first time in Australian waters.

In passing out we saw three Water-Serpents swimming about in the Sea, of a yellow Colour, spotted with dark brown Spots. They were each about four Foot long, and about the bigness of a Man's Wrist, and were the first I saw on this Coast, which abounds with several sorts of them.

This is probably the Olive Sea Snake, *Aipysurus laevis* Lacépède, 1804, family Hydrophiidae, although four other species of the genus occur on the north-west coast. These snakes have flattened tails for propelling themselves through the water. They are highly venomous.

Farther north he wrote on 27 August:

we ... saw many small Dolphins and Whales, and abundance of Scuttle-shells swimming on the Sea; and some Water-snakes every day.

Bottle nose Dolphins, *Tursiops truncatus* (Montagu, 1821), family Delphinidae, are common along the Western Australian coast. They are mammals, not fish, and occur in all tropical and temperate seas, feeding mainly on fish and cephalopods (squid).

On 28 August, when they were probably off North West Cape, they had a rather disturbed night.

we had in the Night abundance of Whales about the Ship, some a head, others a-stern, and some on each side blowing and making a very dismal Noise; but when we came out again into deeper Water they left us. Indeed the Noise that they made by blowing and dashing of the Sea with their Tails, making it all of a Breach and Fome, was very dreadful to us, like the breach of the Waves in very Shole-water, or among Rocks.

These would have been Humpback Whales (see above). Once around the Cape, the *Roebuck* sailed eastwards towards the Dampier Archipelago. Again, sea snakes were abundant, for on 1 September Dampier wrote:

... and as we saw some Sea-snakes every day, so this day we saw a great many, of two different sorts or shapes. One sort was yellow, and about the bigness of a Man's Wrist, about 4 Foot long, having a flat Tail about 4 Fingers broad. The other sort was much smaller and shorter, round and spotted black and yellow.

The larger was probably the Olive Sea Snake (see above), and the smaller possibly the Yellow-bellied Sea Snake, *Pelamis platurus* (Linnaeus, 1766), family Hydrophiidae. This is a widespread species, indeed the only sea snake to be found as far distant as the eastern Pacific Ocean. Otherwise these creatures are confined to the warmer parts of the Indian Ocean and the western Pacific. Twenty-four species of these venomous reptiles have been found along the Western Australian coast.

On that day they anchored off East Lewis Island and went ashore.

We found some Shell-fish, viz. Limpits, Perriwinkles, and Abundance of small Oysters growing on the Rocks, which were very sweet. In the Sea we saw some green Turtle, a pretty many Sharks, and Abundance of Water-Snakes of several sorts and sizes.

A couple of days later as they sailed east from Lewis Island they had a good night's fishing.

In the Night while Calm we fish'd with Hook and Line, and caught good store of Fish, viz. Snappers, Breams, Old Wives, and Dog-fish. When these last came we seldom caught any others; for if they did not drive away the other Fish, yet they would be sure to keep them from taking our Hooks, for they would first have them themselves, biting very greedily. We caught also a Monk-fish, of which I brought home the Picture. See *Fish*, Fig. I.

Snapper may be either seaperch (family Lutjanidae) or emperor fish (family Lethrinidae). The bream was probably the Yellowfin Bream, *Acantho-pagrus latus* (Houttuyn, 1782), family Sparidae. Dampier's figure 4 in Plate 3, labelled the Old Wife, is probably the Triggerfish, *Balistes vetula* Linnaeus, 1785, a species from the Atlantic Ocean; the figure was possibly taken from another book (*vetula* is Latin for 'old woman', old wife being the common name of the fish in the West Indies). Off the north-west coast there is the Starry Triggerfish, *Abalistes stellatus*, which resembles *Balistes vetula* but does not have elongated rays on the dorsal fin. At this locality, his dog-fish were probably small sharks of various genera, common ones here being *Hemi-galeus*, *Rhizoprionodon* and *Triaenodon*, all of the family Carcharhinidae.

By 8 September, they were well out to sea north-east of the Archipelago, and Dampier wrote: 'We saw no Land this Day, but saw a great many Snakes, and some Whales.'

Sealife was also abundant in Lagrange Bay where they were anchored from 9 to 15 September:

The Sea is plentifully stock'd with the largest Whales that I ever saw: but not to compare with the vast ones of the *Northern* Seas. We saw also a great many Green Turtle, but caught none; here being no Place to set a Turtle-Net in; here being no Channel for them, and the Tides running so strong. We saw some Sharks and Parracoots; and with Hooks and Lines we caught some Rock-fish and Old Wives. Of Shell-fish, here were Oysters both the common kind for Eating, and of the Pearl-kind: and also Wilks, Conchs, Muscles, Limpits, Perriwinkles, &c. and I gather'd a few strange Shells; chiefly a sort not large, and thick-set all about with Rays or Spikes growing in Rows.

The 'parracoot' is likely to have been the barracuda, *Leionura atun* (Euphrasen, 1791) family Gempylidae. Dampier was probably familiar with a similar fish in the West Indies known as 'paragood', an old name for barracuda, also spelt barracouta.

The rock fish were probably species of *Epinephelus*, family Serranidae, of which more than 20 species are known from the north-west coast of Western Australia. The shell with 'Rays or Spikes growing in Rows' was probably *Murex pecten* Lightfoot, 1786, a beautiful shell common in northern Australia and the western Pacific. As with the account at Shark Bay, the other shells cannot be identified as there are many species on this coast. 'Wilk' is an old spelling of whelk, spiral-shelled gastropods of the family Buccinidae.

Dampier's last note on marine life in Australian waters was again on sea snakes. On 16 September, as they were sailing north towards Timor, well off the Kimberley coast in latitude 16°09′S, he noted:

This Day we saw two Water-snakes, different in Shape from such as we had formerly seen. The one was very small, though long; the other long and as big as a Man's Leg, having a red Head; which I never saw any have, before or since.

In recognition of Dampier and his observations on sea life, the marine biogeographical province that extends from the Abrolhos Islands, Western Australia, to Torres Strait, Queensland, is called the Dampierian Province (Womersley, 1990).

✳

Land animals

From 16 to 21 August 1699, the *Roebuck* was anchored at Dampier Landing, Dirk Hartog Island. Dampier wrote:

The Land-Animals that we saw here were only a sort of Raccoons, different from those of the *West-Indies*, chiefly as to their Legs; for these have very short fore Legs; but go Jumping upon them as the others do, and like them are very good Meat:) and a Sort of Guano's, of the same shape and size with other Guano's, describ'd [Vol. I. p. 57] but differing from them in three remarkable Particulars: For these had a larger and uglier Head; and had no Tail: And at the Rump, instead of the Tail there, they had a Stump of a Tail, which appear'd like another Head; but not really such, being without Mouth or Eyes: Yet this Creature seem'd by this means to have a Head at each End; and, which may be reckon'd a fourth difference, the Legs also seem'd all four of them to be Fore-legs, being all alike in shape and length, and seeming by the Joints and Bending to be made as if they were to go indifferently either Head or Tail foremost. They were speckled black and yellow like Toads, and had Scales or Knobs on their Backs like those of Crockodiles, plated on to the Skin, or stuck into it, as part of the Skin. They are very slow in motion; and when a Man comes nigh them they will stand still and hiss, not endeavouring to get away. Their Livers are also spotted black and yellow: and the Body when opened hath a very unsavory Smell. I did never see such ugly Creatures any where but here. The Guano's I have observ'd to be very good Meat: And I have often eaten of them with pleasure; but tho' I have eaten of Snakes, Crocodiles, and Allegators, and many Creatures that look frightfully enough, and there are but few I should have been afraid to eat of if prest by Hunger, yet I think my Stomach would scarce have serv'd to venture upon these *N. Holland* Guano's, both the Looks and the Smell of them being so offensive.

Dampier's 'Raccoon' is generally thought to have been the Banded Hare-wallaby, *Lagostrophus fasciatus*, e.g. Ride *in* Ride et al. (1962), Burbidge and George (1978). Formerly common on parts of the mainland, they now survive only on Bernier and Dorre Islands. Baynes (1990) considered this identification unlikely since he was not aware of any definite record from Dirk Hartog Island, but the Western Australian Museum has identified specimens in its collection. Another possibility is a bettong, *Bettongia lesueur* (Quoy & Gaimard, 1824), bones of which have been found on the island. Dampier's is the first description of the hopping movement of Australia's kangaroos, but he did not mention the pouch that characterises our marsupials. Following the wreck of the *Batavia* on the Abrolhos Islands in June 1629, Francisco Pelsaert discovered the Tammar Wallaby (*Macropus eugenii*) and described its pouch, wrongly deducing that the young animal grew from the nipple inside. Willem de Vlamingh, in 1697, mentioned the Quokkas on Rottnest Island but referred to them as forest rats without describing their manner of moving. Nicolaas Witsen, a director of the Dutch East India Company, later referred to the 'pouch below their throats into which one could put one's hand, without being able to understand to what end nature had created the animal like this' (Nelson, 1994).

Dampier's 'Guano' is the Sleepy or Bobtail Lizard, *Tiliqua rugosa* (Gray, 1825). The type specimen of the species was collected on Bernier Island either during the Baudin expedition of 1801–03 or that of de Freycinet in 1818 (there is no collector's name with the specimen). This well-known skink is widespread on the Australian mainland, occurring in States except Northern Territory and Tasmania. It is slow-moving and, when disturbed, turns to face the disturber with an aggressive open-mouthed display rather than scuttling off as do most lizards. It is not venomous. The form on the Shark Bay islands is a distinct subspecies.

Dampier was less expansive about the animals that they saw while at Lagrange Bay from 9 to 15 September:

There are but few Land-Animals. I saw some Lizards; and my Men saw two or three Beasts like hungry Wolves, lean like so many Skeletons, being nothing but Skin and Bones: 'Tis probable that it was the Foot of one of those Beasts that I mention'd as seen by us in *N. Holland* [Vol. I, p. 463]. We saw a Rackoon or two, and one small speckled Snake.

The 'Beasts like hungry Wolves' must have been Dingoes (*Canis lupus dingo* Linnaeus, 1758, family Canidae). Descended from the domestic dog, the Dingo was probably introduced by Aborigines or Asians many thousands of years ago. The 'Rackoon' and small snake cannot be identified. The bush flies bothered them. Dampier wrote: 'while we were at work about the Well we were sadly pester'd with the Flies, which were more troublesome to us than the Sun, tho' it shone clear and strong upon us all the while, very hot'. The Master, Jacob Hughes wrote: 'there is ashoar abundance of small Flyes, which annoyed our people very much in tickling their faces & buzzing about their ears'. These would have been the bush fly (*Musca vetustissima* Walker, 1849), familar to all who have spent time in the Australian bush.

Commemorating Dampier

Literary spinoffs

IT IS GENERALLY ACCEPTED THAT Dampier's travels fired the imagination of later writers, his influence being discussed especially by W.H. Bonner (1934). Samuel Taylor Coleridge referred to him as 'a man of exquisite refinement of mind' and probably gained ideas and inspiration from him for *The Rime of the Ancient Mariner*. Could the albatross that the Mariner shot have had its origin in the petrel shot by Dampier? A member of the Royal Society, on the other hand, wrote that he was 'a blunt fellow, but of better understanding than would have been expected from one of his education' (Lloyd, 1966). Jonathan Swift based *Gulliver's Travels* on his adventures (Gulliver referred to 'my cousin Dampier'). The marooning of Alexander Selkirk (at his own request) by Thomas Stradling on Juan Fernandez Island in 1705 and his 'rescue' in February 1709 by Rogers and Dampier led directly to Daniel Defoe's 'Robinson Crusoe' and 'Captain Singleton'.

The diarist John Evelyn mentioned dining with Samuel Pepys on 16 August [Julian 6 August] 1698 'where was Captain Dampier, who had been a famous buccaneer, had brought hither the painted prince Job, and printed a relation of his very strange adventure ... He was now going abroad again by the King's encouragment, who furnished a ship of 290 tons. He seemed a more modest man than one would imagine by relation of the crew he had associated with'. By then Pepys himself was blind and had long since ceased writing his diary, otherwise we might have had a more detailed, firsthand account of a fascinating character. The 'painted prince' was Jeoly, a tattooed Filipino, brought to England by Dampier and an associate for display to the public. Both sold their shares in him, and his fate thereafter is unknown.

The later literature on Dampier is large and includes several biographies. The most recent of these (Gill, 1997, pp. 372–373) gives a list of the editions of his journals held at the British Library. It is interesting to note that the poet T.S. Eliot also came from East Coker. One of his poems, perhaps inspired by Dampier, is on a plaque in St Michael's Church in the village:

> Old men ought to be explorers
> Here or there does not matter
> We must be still and still moving
> Into another intensity
> For a further union, a deeper communion
> Through the dark cold and empty isolation,
> The wave cry, the wind cry, the vast waters
> Of the petrel and the porpoise. In the end is my beginning.

Memorials

In St Michael's parish church at East Coker, Somerset, are two memorials to Dampier. One is a plaque, placed by the local community and unveiled on 19 May 1908, with the inscription:

TO THE MEMORY OF
WILLIAM DAMPIER
BUCCANEER EXPLORER HYDROGRAPHER
and sometime Captain of the Ship Roebuck
in the Royal Navy of King William the Third.
Thrice he circumnavigated the Globe
and first of all Englishmen
explored and described the coast of Australia
An exact observer
of all things in Earth, Sea and Air
he recorded the knowledge won by years of
danger and hardship in Books of Voyages
and a Discourse of Winds, Tides and Currents
which Nelson bade his midshipmen to study
and Humboldt praised for Scientific worth

Born at East Coker in 1651
he died in London in 1715
and lies buried in an unknown grave

"The World is apt to judge of everything by the
Success and whoso has ill Fortune
will hardly be allowed a good name"

The other was erected by the Government of Western Australia for the tercentenary of Dampier's first landing in Australia. Unveiled by the then Agent-General for Western Australia Ron Davies on 4 September 1988, it reads:

To the memory of William Dampier, Buccaneer, Explorer, Hydrographer and sometime Captain of the Ship Roebuck in the Royal Navy of King William III.

At Broome, Western Australia, in Bedford Park facing Roebuck Bay there is a monument to Dampier in the form of a carved granite sea chest. Beside it is a plaque inscribed 'This memorial chest was presented to the towns people of Broome by the Commonwealth Government and the W.A. Historical Society and unveiled by Commander R.R. Dowling R.A.N., H.M.A.S. Swan on the 30th October 1938'. On the side of the chest is Dampier's coat of arms and the words 'William Dampier 1652 1715' [at the time it was believed that he was born in 1652]. The Poet Laureate of the day, John Masefield, prepared a dedicatory oration including a verse inscribed on the top of the chest:

> We little guess which deed
> a future year
> may mark to mortals, from
> our passing here.

In 1955, a Perth department store, Boans Ltd, presented a display window featuring Dampier to the Western Australian Museum but it appears be no longer extant.

Dampier is one of 16 explorers (and four ships) shown in bas-relief on four bronze panels at the entrance to the Mitchell Library, State Library of New South Wales, Sydney. They were designed by the sculptor Arthur Fleischmann, donated by Sir William Dixson, and inaugurated when the Library was completed in 1942 (Jones, 1988).

Three Australian postage stamps have commemorated Dampier. The first, with a value of five shillings and designed by W. Jardine, was issued on 25 November 1964, featuring a portrait with a sailing ship in the background. It was reissued on 14 February 1966 (the date of conversion to decimal currency in Australia) with a value of 50 cents. In 1985 a 33 cent stamp designed by Garry Emery, based on the Thomas Murray portrait and with parts of the coastal profiles from Dampier's journal, appeared both as a sheet and as one of four in a miniature sheet that also featured Abel Tasman, a detail from a painting by J.G. Cuyp of Tasman and his family dated c.1637, and Dirk Hartog's ship *Eendracht*. The background is part of a 1622 map by Hessel Gerritsz, the first to show the west side of Cape York Peninsula discovered in 1606 by Willem Jansz. On 19 March 1999, the 1966 stamp was reissued with a value of 45 cents. It appeared in a miniature sheet together with stamps of Phillip Parker King and George Bass. A second sheet reproduced early stamps of Tasman, James Cook and Matthew Flinders. This issue was designed by Cozzolini/Ellett Designs Division (Phil Ellett).

A number of places, features, plants and animals are named after Dampier (see Eponymy below).

What of the landing sites today?

All four of Dampier's landing sites in 1699, as well as that of 1688, remain in a natural or near-natural state. Karrakatta Bay, the site of the 1688 landing, is on an Aboriginal reserve managed by the One Arm Point community. It probably is much the same now as it was then. There are some obscure vehicle tracks but otherwise the area appears undisturbed.

Most of Dirk Hartog Island is a pastoral lease and is stocked with sheep, but the numbers are low and little or no grazing now occurs towards the northern end where Dampier landed. Cape Inscription and the adjacent area containing the lighthouse are reserved land. Inland from Dampier's landing site there are several vehicle tracks that are little-used, and the vegetation is in excellent condition with only minor weed establishment.

Bernier Island, where several of the crew landed, is (together with the nearby Dorre Island) an A class reserve for conservation of flora and fauna. Apart from a few small ruins where a hospital stood early this century there is little disturbance on the island.

East Lewis Island is reserved for conservation and recreation; indeed, most islands of the Dampier Archipelago are included in a conservation reserve.

The central and northern parts of Lagrange Bay (including Dampier's presumed landing site) are reserved for use by the Bidyadanga Aboriginal community, and the remainder is included in the Frazier Downs pastoral lease. The vegetation remains in a good state, although Birdwood Grass (*Cenchrus setiger* Vahl) that was introduced early as a pasture-improver is very common on the plains. A number of vehicle tracks criss-cross the area.

Eponymy

Dampier and his ships have been commemorated in a number of names of places, plants, animals, geological features and a naval ship.

Places in Australia

Dampier (town), 20°39′50″S, 116°42′43″E. Established by Hamersley Iron Company in 1966 as a port for exporting iron ore. Gazetted on 30 June 1972.

Dampier Archipelago, which includes all islands between Victoria Rock (20°43′S, 116°24′E) and Delambre Island (20°26′S, 117°04′E). Named by Louis de Freycinet on the Baudin expedition in March 1803.

Dampier Creek, 17°56′4″S, 122°14′5″E, a short creek flowing into Roebuck Bay. Named by J.E. Coghlan when surveying the area in 1883.

Dampier Downs (pastoral station), 18°24′S, 123°06′E, south-east of Broome.

Dampier Hill, 17°28′S, 123°02′E, on the Dampier Peninsula west of Derby. An unofficial name.

Dampier Landing, 25°31′S, 113°00′E, Dirk Hartog Island, formerly known as Sammys; the site of Dampier's first landing on his visit of 1699 (on 17 August), marked with a commemorative plaque to be unveiled on 17 August 1999. Name proposed by Phillip Playford.

Dampierland, Dampier Land, Dampier Peninsula. These are unofficial names but have been commonly used in scientific papers for the large peninsula between Broome and Derby.

Dampiers Monument, 16°07′37″S, 123°26′22″E, an island in the Buccaneer Archipelago. Named by Phillip Parker King on 20 August 1821.

Dampier Reef, 25°21′21″S, 113°04′29″E, off the south end of Dorre Island.

Dampier Road, 25°33′20″S, 113°25′07″E, a sea channel near the north end of Peron Peninsula.

Dampier Rock, 34°16′50″S, 122°21′05″E, in the Archipelago of the Recherche. Included on an admiralty chart after surveys by J.W. Combe in 1900–01.

Dampier Botanical District. Name bestowed by John Beard in 1979 for a vegetation district of the south-western Kimberley (Beard, 1979).

Dampierian Province, for the near-coastal marine biogeographical environment of Australia from the Abrolhos Islands, Western Australia, to Torres Strait, Queensland. Name proposed in 1904 by C. Hedley.

Cygnet Bay, 16°34′44″S, 122°58′52″E, on the west side of King Sound. Named by Phillip Parker King on 20 August 1821.

Cygnet Hill, 16°27′09″S, 123°03′17″E, near Karrakatta Bay. Named during hydrographic surveys in 1909–13

Cygnet Park, 17°56′10″S, 122°13′54″E, a park in Broome, named in February 1998.

Roebuck Bay, 18°05′14″S, 122°16′5″E. Named by Phillip Parker King on 26 August 1821.

Roebuck Deep, 17°59'30"S, 122°09'32"E, a deep channel off Gantheaume Point, near Broome. Named by J.E. Coghlan when surveying the area in 1883.

Roebuck Plains, 17°57'S, 122°26'E, a vast plain east and south of Broome. Name first used in 1962, by the Australian Army.

Roebuck Plains, 17°55'56"S, 122°28'16"E, a pastoral station east of Broome, first leased by E.W. Streeter in 1886 so it is likely that the name dates from then.

A number of streets in the suburbs of Perth are named after Dampier, the *Cygnet* and the *Roebuck*. Two are named Dampiera, after the blue-flowered plants that commemorate him.

Buccaneer Archipelago, a group of islands lying off Yampi Sound, north of Derby. Named by Phillip Parker King on 20 August 1821.

Places elsewhere
Cape Dampier, on the south coast of New Britain.

Dampier Island (= Karkar), off the north-east coast of New Guinea.

Dampier Spring, Ascension Island (discovered and used by Dampier's crew during their stay there in 1701).

Dampier Strait, between New Britain and Umboi [island], Bismarck Archipelago.

Selat Dampier, a strait between Waigeo [island] and West Irian.

Plants
Beaufortia dampieri (Myrtaceae), a bottlebrush with small pink flowers, named by William J. Hooker in 1833, using a name proposed by Allan Cunningham. Now a synonym of *Beaufortia sprengelioides* (A.P. de Candolle) Craven.

Dampiera (Goodeniaceae), a genus of mainly blue-flowered plants, named by Robert Brown in 1810.

Diplolaena dampieri (Rutaceae), named by René Désfontaines in 1817 (but not the species that Dampier collected).

Eucalyptus dampieri (Myrtaceae), a bloodwood eucalypt named by Denis J. Carr & S.G. Maisie Carr in 1987. Not collected by Dampier.

Westringia dampieri (Lamiaceae), named by Robert Brown in 1810. Not collected by Dampier.

Willdampia (Fabaceae) named by Alex George in 1999. This is the Sturt Pea, previously known as *Swainsona formosa*, and before that as *Clianthus formosus*. Another early name no longer used is *Clianthus dampieri*.

Animals

Many of these commemorate Dampier indirectly, being named after the Dampierian Province or the Dampier Archipelago.

Fish

Dampieria (Pseudochromidae), published by Castelnau in 1875 but no longer an accepted name. These are dottyback fishes that live along Australia's northern coast. Two species described under the name are now synonyms of *Labracinus*, and two others are placed in *Pseudochromis*.

Dampierosa (Scorpaenidae) named by Gilbert P. Whitley in 1932. This is a scorpionfish endemic along the north-west coast of Western Australia.

Dampierosoma daruma (Scorpaenidae) named by Gilbert P. Whitley in 1932. This is a stonefish of the north-west coast.

Snails

Acrosterigma dampierense Wilson & Stevenson, 1977 (Mollusca: Bivalvia: Cardiidae), a cockle.

Amoria dampieria Weaver, 1960 (Mollusca: Gastropoda: Volutidae), a volute.

Conus dampierensis Coomans & Filmer, 1985 (Mollusca: Gastropoda: Conidae), a cone shell.

Fusiaphera dampierensis Garrard, 1975 (Mollusca: Gastropoda: Cancellariidae), a cancellarid.

Gemmula dampierana Powell, 1964 (Mollusca: Gastropoda: Turridae), a turrid.

Glycymeris dampierensis Matsukuma, 1984 (Mollusca: Gastropoda: Glycymeriidae), a dog cockle.

Rhagada dampieriana Solem, 1997 (Mollusca: Gastropoda: Camaenidae), a land snail.

Splendrillia dampieria (Hedley, 1922) (Mollusca: Gastropoda: Turridae), a turrid.

Crustacean
Uca vocans dampieri Crane, 1975 (Crustacea, Decapoda: Ocypodidae), a fiddler crab.

Sea spider
Rhopalorhynchus dampieri Child, 1975 (Pycnogonida: Colossendeidae), a sea spider.

Geological names
Dampier Granitoid Complex, a granite-greenstone structural unit along the coast near Karratha, probably about 3000 million years old.

Dampier Limestone, a soft rock occurring along the peninsulas of Shark Bay and the adjacent islands, thought to be about 240 000 years old.

Dampier Sub-basin, a geological unit lying off the north-west coast of Western Australia.

Ships
A Royal Naval survey ship is named HMS *Dampier* in his honour.

In March 1999, the first of eight 'Bay Class' surveillance ships being built in Fremantle for Australian Customs was launched as ACV *Roebuck Bay*.

Appendix

Matters of fact and opinion

I believe that a number of errors have crept into writings on Dampier. Misdeterminations of the Australian plants by previous authors are discussed under the relevant species above, but several erroneous records and other matters on which there have been various interpretations are discussed here.

Dampier's year of birth has commonly been given as 1652 but, as shown by several writers (e.g. Lloyd, 1966), it was 1651. Another William Dampier was born there the following year.

It has commonly been stated or implied (e.g. Clark, 1962; Lloyd, 1966; Yarrow, 1980) that Dampier was the first Englishman to land on the Australian mainland, but there is no evidence to show that he, rather than another of the crew of the *Cygnet*, was first ashore. Indeed, in describing this visit of 1688, writers generally have not given enough credit to the captain of the ship, John Reed (Read). Dampier's rank on the ship is unknown. The first Englishmen to land on Australian territory were from the East India Company ship *Trial* when it was wrecked in May 1622 on rocks that now bear the ship's name near the Monte Bello Islands, off the north-west coast.

Aeschynomene indica was listed by Osborn and Gardner (1939) but Dampier's specimen was not collected in New Holland (George, 1971).

Dampier's specimen of *Casuarina equisetifolia* was attributed to New Holland by Ray (1705) and accepted as an Australian record by Osborn and Gardner (1939) and Hamilton and Bruce (1998), but not by George

(1971) or N.G. Marchant (1988, p. 197). The species is common on tropical coasts from Burma to Polynesia but has not been recorded in Western Australia, and Dampier's specimen was probably collected in Timor or New Guinea.

Although he acknowledged that a cup-shaped style-end occurs in Lobeliaceae (now usually placed in Campanulaceae) as well as Goodeniaceae, N.G. Marchant (1988, p. 196) determined Tab. 2, figure 2 [correctly figure 1] (described by Ray as '*Rapuntium* Novæ Hollandiæ') as *Scaevola tomentosa*; but this figure does in fact represent a South American species of *Centropogon* (Campanulaceae), as explained by Osborn and Gardner. Dampier must have confused the locality when attributing it to New Holland. Scott-Child (1992) repeated the error.

Osborn and Gardner (1939) expressed surprise that Dampier did not collect *Acacia aneura*, the Mulga tree widespread in arid Australia, but the species does not occur on the coast and would not have been seen by Dampier (George, 1971). Curiously, they stated that Dampier visited during the dry season: while this is true for the Dampier Archipelago and Lagrange Bay, it is not for Dirk Hartog Island which receives most of its rain in winter.

L.R. Marchant and N.G. Marchant (1988, pp. 115, 194) considered Dampier's Dragon Tree of the 1688 visit to be a species of *Pandanus* since these 'are the only trees of any significance in the area described by Dampier' and because the Dragon Tree (*Dracaena draco*) looks 'remarkably like the Screw Pines' (*Pandanus*). Beken (1998) further confused the matter by stating that the Dragon Tree is 'a tree which produces gum-tragacanth', the latter 'a resin used in medicine as a drug medium'. Tragacanth is a gum obtained from several species of the legume genus *Astragalus*, but these are small shrubby plants and could not be compared with apple-sized trees. The vegetation west of the beach at Karrakatta Bay where the *Cygnet* was careened is, in fact, a savannah woodland of various trees including *Pandanus*, *Ficus*, *Pouteria*, *Acacia*, *Melaleuca* and *Eucalyptus*. A bloodwood eucalypt named *Eucalyptus dampieri* in 1987 after Dampier is common the woodland. Towards Swan Point the trees become sparse and are mainly *Pandanus*. Dampier's description of the trees as 'the bigness of our Apple-trees' with 'Leaves of a dark colour' and gum distilling 'out of Knots or Cracks' in the bark fits bloodwoods, but not pandanus. Gum does not seep from the trunk of pandanus, nor does it have a rough, cracked bark, and the leaves are usually pale bluish or yellowish green. It is almost certain that Dampier was referring to the red gum, rather than to the growth form, when he described them as Dragon Trees. This interpretation was accepted by Hamilton and Bruce (1998). The illustration included by L.R. Marchant (1988, p. 115) with the caption 'The Dragon Tree seen in the Kimberleys and recorded by Dampier who confused it with the Pandanus Palm' is of a dragon tree in the Cape Verde Islands, taken (as stated, op. cit. p. xv) from D. Defoe, *The Four Years Voyages of Captain George Roberts*, London, 1726.

L.R. Marchant (1988, p. 135) misinterpreted the mention of grass by Dampier at the anchorage near Bernier and Dorre Islands, unless he had in mind the master Jacob Hughes' account. The grass referred to by Dampier was a species of *Triodia* seen by members of his crew on Bernier Island, not seagrass. Their soundings in Shark Bay showed a bottom of clean sand at all three anchorages. Dampier did not mention seagrass, but Hughes, as a general observation, described 'Long Grass which maketh black and white water ... these white waters give us notice of the Sheltings' (i.e. shelvings or sand banks). Twelve species of seagrass have been identified in Shark Bay (Walker, 1992).

N.G. Marchant (1988, p. 195) considered that the trees 'sweet-scented, and reddish within the Bark, like Sassafras, but redder' seen on Dirk Hartog Island were *Clerodendrum lanceolatum*, repeating an error by Mueller (1883) but, as pointed out by George (1971), this was a misdetermination of a figure representing a South American plant. *Clerodendrum* has not been recorded on Dirk Hartog Island. The tree may have been *Pittosporum phylliraeoides* or *Alectryon oleifolius*, both of which have been recorded there.

Hamilton and Bruce (1998) stated that, on his 1688 visit, Dampier landed 'near present-day Broome, Cygnet Bay in the Pilbara', but Marchant (1988) has shown that it was probably at Karrakatta Bay near Cape Leveque; Cygnet Bay is in King Sound, and the Pilbara region is farther south. They also wrote that 'For the white man who did not know the secret of its plants, Australia was the "Scurvy Coast" ' but this name has not been used previously. The illness does not seem to have been any more of a problem for early mariners along this coast than elsewhere [see p. 150]. Hamilton and Bruce wrote that Dampier 'unwittingly described the dark red heavy iron ore in the rocks' but many rocks in arid regions of Australia are weathered red, and those described by Dampier as 'all of a rusty Colour, and Ponderous' (on East Lewis Island) are a kind of granophyre, not the iron-ore-bearing rocks of the Pilbara (Kriewaldt, 1964) [see p. 150]. Hamilton and Bruce mentioned 'gum-tree leaves' as one of the specimens seen by John Ray but, as mentioned above, Dampier probably saw none during the 1699 visit except possibly at Lagrange Bay; there is no eucalypt among his specimens or among the plants described by Ray. The numbers cited by Hamilton and Bruce for Australian specimens described by Ray and Plukenet may be amended in view of research discussed above (pp 22, 23). The nine described by Ray and the eight by Plukenet are all extant at Oxford, except the *Acanthocarpus* and *Ptilotus*.

Spencer (1981) gave 'in the vicinity of Roebuck Bay' as the location of Dampier's third landing site of 1699, instead of Lagrange Bay.

Dampier's 'raccoon' on Dirk Hartog Island is generally thought (e.g. Ride *in* Ride et al., 1962; Burbidge and George, 1978) to have been the Banded Hare-wallaby, *Lagostrophus fasciatus* (Péron & Lesueur, 1807). Baynes (1990) believed that this species had not been recorded for the island, but it is now known to be represented by specimens in the Western Australian Museum. Formerly common on Dirk Hartog Island and the adjacent mainland, it now survives only on Bernier and Dorre Islands.

A moss collected by Dampier was first described by the German-born English botanist Johann Dillenius in his *Historia Muscorum* of 1741, p. 364, as 'Bryum candidum fragile, foliis recurvis. *The white brittle Bryum, with crooked Leafes'* [sic], with an illustration, and said to be from New Holland. He saw a specimen from Dampier's collection in the Sherardian Herbarium at Oxford. Later researchers overlooked the record until the 1950s when the specimen was again related to the figure in Dillenius' work, although the drawing shows a fertile specimen and those now extant at Oxford are sterile (Downing and Marner, 1998). Although this moss — *Leucobryum candidum* (A.M.F.J.P. de Beauvois) Wilson — occurs in Australia (in the Northern Territory and eastern Australian States), as well as on islands to the north and in Southeast Asia, it has now been argued that Dampier's specimen could not have come from Australia since his landing sites are too dry. It was probably collected in Timor or New Guinea. Whatever its source, it is certainly the first moss collected by a European in the Southeast Asian region.

Gill (1997) seems to have been confused over Dampier's landing and collecting sites in 1699, not mentioning Dirk Hartog Island but stating the the plant specimens were collected 'probably on Enderby [which Dampier did not visit] and East Lewis Islands' and that Dampier 'touched at Rosemary Island' (see above for discussion). Later Gill wrote that on 30 August (Julian calendar) they were 'near the area now known as Dampier Land', possibly confusing the two voyages as it was on the 1688 visit that Dampier landed there. Gill also used the long-discarded name *Clianthus dampieri* for Sturt Pea, and considered that the identity of the 'hippopotamus' found in a shark at Shark Bay could not be determined (it was a Dugong). He stated wrongly that the *Roebuck* was careened at Shark Bay (it was scrubbed, a different procedure), and that the town of Dampier was founded in 1860 (it was 1966).

The adjustment of the dates given in Dampier's journal has been discussed by several authors, notably L.R. Marchant (1988, p. 63) and Gill (1997), but their conclusion that 11 days should be added is only partially correct. When Pope Gregory XIII issued a papal bull decreeing that after 4 October 1582 ten days should be added to adjust for the error that had accumulated since the introduction of the Julian calendar in 45 BC, the change was adopted by some, but not all, countries. Others followed on various dates, the last being China in 1949. Britain and its dependencies made the change in September 1752, 11 days being added so that the day after 2 September became not 3 but 14 September. The eleventh day was inserted since, in Britain, still under the Julian calendar, 1700 was considered a leap year, hence included 29 February, but under the Gregorian calendar 1700 was not a leap year (Duncan, 1998). Thus for British dates the adjustment by adding 11 days is correct only for dates after 28 February 1700. Authors adjusting dates in Dampier's journals have assumed that 11 days should be added throughout, but in fact it should be only ten up to and including that date; this applies to both of his visits to New Holland. On 28 February 1700, Dampier was off the north-east of New Ireland, and all dates thereafter on this and his later voyages must be amended by 11 days.

A number of writers (e.g. Steven, 1988; L.R. Marchant, 1988, p. 24) have commented that Dampier was unimpressed by the western Australian coast and its hinterland. Certainly, he was disappointed at the lack of water, the absence of anything of economic value, and what he considered the poor circumstances of the Aborigines; yet he was clearly intrigued by its natural history, otherwise he would not have examined it in such detail. He mentioned 'very sweet and fragrant' flowers, small flowers that were 'sweet and beautiful', and the Sturt Pea as 'looking very beautiful'. Similarly, he wrote of 'many sorts of very strange and beautiful Shells'.

Footnote added in proof

The Duchess of Hamilton has suggested that I am wrong to interpret their use of the term 'Scurvy Coast' as though it had been generally applied to the Australian coast. She wrote: 'it was, in fact, a device used by us to describe the appearance of the coast to early Europeans'.

Additional reference

Kriewaldt, M. (1964). *Dampier and Barrow Island, W.A.* Western Australian Geological Survey 1:250 000 Geological Series Explanatory Notes.

Bibliography

Baudin, N. (1974). *The Journal of Post Captain Nicolas Baudin Commander-in-Chief of the Corvettes* Géographe *and* Naturaliste, translated by C. Cornell. Libraries Board of South Australia, Adelaide.

Baynes, A. (1990). The mammals of Shark Bay, Western Australia. Pages 313–325 in P.F. Berry, S.D. Bradshaw and B.R. Wilson (eds), *Research in Shark Bay: Report of the France–Australe Bicentenary Expedition Committee*. Western Australian Museum, [Perth].

Beaglehole, J.C. (1962). *The* Endeavour *Journal of Joseph Banks 1768–1771*. Angus & Robertson, Sydney.

Beard, J.S. (1979). *Vegetation Survey of Western Australia: Kimberley 1: 1 000 000 Vegetation Series, Explanatory notes to sheet 1, The Vegetation of the Kimberley Area*. University of Western Australia Press, Nedlands.

Brummitt, R.K. and Powell, C.E. (1992). *Authors of Plant Names*. Royal Botanic Gardens, Kew.

Burbidge, A.A. and George, A.S. (1978). The flora and fauna of Dirk Hartog Island, Western Australia. *Journal of the Royal Society of Western Australia* **60**: 71–90.

Carr, D.J. (1983). The books that sailed with the *Endeavour*. *Endeavour*, new series, 7: 194–201.

Chapman, A.D. and Maslin, B.R. (1992). *Acacia* Miscellany 5. A review of the *A. bivenosa* group (Leguminosae: Mimosoideae: Section *Phyllodineae*). *Nuytsia* **8**: 249–283.

Clark, C.M.H. (1962). *A History of Australia*. Vol. I. Melbourne University Press, Carlton.

Clokie, H.N. (1964). *An Account of the Herbaria of the Department of Botany in the University of Oxford*. Oxford University Press, Oxford.

The Compact Oxford English Dictionary (1991). 2nd edn. Clarendon Press, Oxford.

Cowan, R.S. and Maslin, B.R. (1993). *Acacia* Miscellany 9. The taxonomic status of *Acacia coriacea* (Leguminosae: Mimosoideae: Section *Plurinerves*). *Nuytsia* **9**: 83–90.

Craven, L. (1999). Typification of the name *Regelia* and transfer of *Melaleuca sprengelioides* to *Beaufortia* (Myrtaceae). *Taxon* **48**: 53–55.

Dampier, W. (1697). *A New Voyage Round the World*. James Knapton, London.

Dampier, W. (1699). *A Discourse of Trade-winds, Breezes, Storms, Seasons of the Year, Tides and Currents of the Torrid Zone throughout the World*. James Knapton, London.

Dampier, W. (1703). *A Voyage to New Holland &c in the Year 1699*. James Knapton, London.

Dampier, W. (1709). *Continuation of a Voyage to New Holland &c in the Year 1699*. James Knapton, London.

Dampier, W. (1998). *A New Voyage Round the World*, ed. M. Beken. hummingbird press, London.

Downing, A. and Marner, S. (1998). The first moss to be collected in Australia? *Leucobryum candidum* — collected by William Dampier in 1699. *Bryological Notes* **20**: 237–240.

Ducker, S.C. (1990). History of Australian Marine Phycology. Pages 415–430 in M.N. Clayton and R.J. King (eds), *Marine Botany: An Australian Perspective*. Longman Cheshire, Melbourne.

Duncan, D.E. (1998). *The Calendar*. Fourth Estate, London.

Everist, S.L. (1974). *Poisonous Plants of Australia*. Angus & Robertson, Sydney.

Finney, C.M. (1984). *To Sail Beyond the Sunset: Natural History in Australia 1699–1829*. Rigby, Adelaide.

George, A.S. (1971). The plants seen and collected in north-western Australia by William Dampier. *The Western Australian Naturalist* **11**: 173–178.

George, A.S. (1999). *Willdampia*, a new generic name for Sturt Pea. *The Western Australian Naturalist* **22**: 191–193.

Gill, A. (1997). *The Devil's Mariner: A Life of William Dampier, Pirate and Explorer, 1651–1715*. Michael Joseph, London.

Greuter, W. et al. (1994). *International Code of Botanical Nomenclature (Tokyo Code)*. Koeltz Scientific Books, Königstein.

Hamilton, Jill, Duchess of, and Bruce, Julia (1998). *The Flower Chain: The Early Discovery of Australian Plants*. Kangaroo Press, an imprint of Simon & Schuster Australia, East Roseville.

Henrey, B. (1975). *British Botanical and Horticultural Literature before 1800*. Vol. 1. Oxford University Press, London.

Hopper, S.D., Purdie, R.W., George, A.S. and Patrick, S.J. (1987). *Conostylis*. In A.S. George (ed.), *Flora of Australia* **46**: 57–110.

Kenneally, K.F., Edinger, D.C. and Willing, T. (1996). *Broome and Beyond: Plants and People of the Dampier Peninsula, Kimberley, Western Australia.* Department of Conservation and Land Management, Como.

Lazarides, M. (1997). A revision of *Triodia* including *Plectrachne* (Poaceae, Eragrostideae, Triodiinae). *Australian Systematic Botany* **10**: 381–489.

Linnaeus, C. (1753). *Species Plantarum.* Lars Salvius, Stockholm.

Lloyd, C. (1966). *William Dampier.* Faber and Faber, London.

Mabberley, D.J. (1987). *The Plant Book.* Cambridge University Press, Cambridge.

Maiden, J.H. (1909). Records of Western Australian Botanists. *Journal of the Western Australian Natural History Society* **6**: 5–33.

Marchant, L.R. (1988). *An Island unto Itself: William Dampier and New Holland.* Hesperian Press, Victoria Park.

Marchant, N.G. (1988). The Observations on Western Australian flora made by William Dampier. Pages 194–197 in Marchant, L.R., *An Island unto Itself: William Dampier and New Holland.* Hesperian Press, Victoria Park.

Marrero, A., Almeida, R.S. and González-Martín, M. (1998). A new species of the wild dragon tree, *Dracaena* (Dracaenaceae) from Gran Canaria and its taxonomic and biogeographic implications. *Botanical Journal of the Linnean Society* **128**: 291–314.

Maslin, B.R. (1978). Studies in the genus *Acacia* (Mimosaceae) — 8. A revision of the *Uninerves-Triangulares*, in part (the tetramerous species). *Nuytsia* **2**: 266–333.

Morphy, H. and Edwards, E. (1988). *Australia in Oxford.* Pitt Rivers Museum, Oxford.

Mueller, F. (1883). *The Plants Indigenous around Sharks Bay and its Vicinity*. Parliamentary Paper no. 26. Government Printer, Perth.

Nelson, E.C. (1994). Nicolaas Witsens' letter of 1698 to Martin Lister about a Dutch expedition to the South Land (Western Australia): the original text and a review of its significance for the history of Australian natural history. *Archives of Natural History* **21**: 147–167.

Osborn, T.G.B. and Gardner, C.A. (1939). Dampier's Australian Plants. *Proceedings of the Linnean Society of London* Session 151, part 2: 44–50.

Playford, P. (1996). *Carpet of Silver, The Wreck of the Zuytdorp*. University of Western Australian Press, Nedlands.

Playford, P. (1998). *Voyage of Discovery to Terra Australis by Willem de Vlamingh in 1696–97*. Western Australian Museum, Perth.

Plukenet, L. (1705). *Amaltheum Botanicum*. The author, London.

Ray, J. (1704). *Historiæ Plantarum* vol. 3. Smith & Walford, London.

Ride, W.D.L. et al. (1985). *International Code of Zoological Nomenclature*. International Trust for Zoological Nomenclature in association with British Musuem (Natural History), London.

Ride, W.D.L., Mees, G.F., Douglas, A.M., Royce, R.D. and Tyndale-Biscoe, C.H. (1962). *The Results of an Expedition to Bernier and Dorre Islands Shark Bay, Western Australia in July, 1959*. Fauna Bulletin No. 2, Fisheries Department, Perth.

Scott-Child, R. (1992). *Pirates Don't Pick Flowers*. Literary Mouse Press, Kalamunda.

Semeniuk, V., Kenneally, K.F. and Wilson, P.G. (1978). *Mangroves of Western Australia*. Handbook no. 12. Western Australian Naturalists' Club, Nedlands.

Serventy, D.L. and Whittell, H.M. (1962). *Birds of Western Australia*, 3rd edn. Paterson Brokensha, Perth.

Smith, A.W., revised W.T. Stearn (1972). *A Gardener's Dictionary of Plant Names*. Cassell, London.

Smith, B. (1979). Art as Information: Reflections on the Art from Captain Cook's Voyages. Annual lecture delivered to the Australian Academy of the Humanities at its Ninth Annual General Meeting at Canberra on 16 May 1978. Sydney University Press, Sydney.

Spencer, J. (ed.) (1981). *A Voyage to New Holland: The English Voyage of Discovery to the South Seas in 1699: William Dampier*. Allan Sutton, Gloucester.

Stafleu, F.A. and Cowan, R.S. (1983). *Taxonomic Literature*, 2nd edn, vol. 4. Bohn, Scheltema & Holkema, Utrecht/Antwerpen.

Stanbury, P.J. (1987). The discovery of the Australian fauna and the establishment of collections. Pages 202–226 in G.R. Dyne and D.W. Walton (eds), *Fauna of Australia* Vol. 1A. Australian Government Publishing Service, Canberra.

Stearn, W.T. (1957). Introduction to facsimile of first edition of Carl Linnaeus, *Species Plantarum*. Vol. 1, pp. 1–134. Ray Society, London.

Steven, M. (1988). *First Impressions: The British Discovery of Australia*. British Museum (Natural History), London.

Thompson, J. (1990). New species and combinations in the genus *Swainsona*. *Telopea* **4**: 1–5.

Thompson, J. (1993). A revision of the genus *Swainsona* (Fabaceae). *Telopea* **5**: 427–581.

Tuckfield, T. (1955). William Dampier — where did he land? *Journal and Proceedings of the Western Australian Historical Society* **5**: 5–15.

Walker, D. (1992). Grasses of the sea. *Landscope* **7** (2): 42–46.

Williamson, J.A. (ed.) (1939). *A Voyage to New Holland by William Dampier*. The Argonaut Press, [London].

Wilson, P.G., Armstrong, J.A. and Griffin, E.A. (1998). *Diplolaena* (Rutaceae), new taxa and nomenclatural notes. *Nuytsia* **12**: 107–118.

Womersley, H.B.S. (1990). Biogeography of Australasian Marine Macroalgae. Pages 367–381 in M.N. Clayton and R.J. King (eds), *Marine Botany: An Australian Perspective*. Longman Cheshire, Melbourne.

Yarrow, S. (1980). *We Discovered an Island*. Regency Publications, Booragoon.

Index

A

Abalistes stellatus, 106, 129
Aborigines, 5, 14
Abrolhos Islands, 8, 107
Abrus precatorius, 16
  subsp. *precatorius*, **84**, 96
Acacia, 3, 10, 16, 24, 61
  aneura, 146
  coriacea, 24, **45**, 61
  ligulata, 23, 26, **46**, 62
  rostellifera, 62
  truncata, 3
Acanthocarpus, 23, 25, 26
  robustus, 27, **85**, 96
Acrosterigma dampierense, 143
Adriana, 23, 26, 62
  tomentosa, **47**, 62
Aegialitis, 16
Aeschynomene indica, 145
Agardh, Carl Adolph, 95
Aipysurus laevis, **121**, 127
Alcea, 74
Alectryon oleifolius, 10, 147
alga, 107
alligator pike, 107
Alyogyne, 10
  pinoniana, xvi, 89, 97

Amaltheum Botanicum, 22, **42**, **43**, **44**
Amelanchier, 68
Amoria dampieria, 143
Anas gibberfrons, 102
Ancient Mariner, Rime of the, 135
angel shark, 105
Anglesey, 17
animal names, xv
  authors of, xvi
  starting date of
    nomenclature, xvi
Anous stolidus, 104, **112**
*Anthus novaeseelandiae
  australis*, 102
Aptychotrema vincentiana, **119**, 125
Aquila audax, 102
Ascension Island, 17, 142
Astragalus, 146
Australian Gannet, 101
Australian Pelican, 102
Australian Sea Lion, 108, **118**
authors of animal names, xvi
authors of plant names, xvi
Avicennia marina, **37**
Avocet, Red-necked, 102, 110

B

Bahia, 8, 25
Balistes vetula, 106, **116**, 129
Banded Hare-wallaby, **123**, 131, 148
barracouta, 130
barracuda, 129
Bass, George, 139
Batavia, 2
Batchelor's Delight, xviii, 4
Baudin, Thomas Nicholas, 13, 19,
    61, 68, 69, 73, 75, 132, 140
Bauhinia, 16
Beach Morning Glory, 87
Beach Spinifex, **89**
beans, 13, 15, 16
Beaufortia, 10, 22, 23, 26, 63
    dampieri, 63, 75, 142
    sprengelioides, **34**, 48, 63, 142
Beauvois, Palisot de, 73
Bedford Park, Broome, 124
Bentham, George, 23, 62, 65
Bernier Island, 12, **34**, 139
bettong, 132
Bettongia lesueur, 132
Bidyadanga, 140
bird song, 102
birdflower, 13
    Green, **87**
Birdwood Grass, 140
Black Swan, 2
Black-and-white Fairy-wren, 102
blanquillo, 106, **113**
    Blue, 106
    Flagtail, 106
bloodwood, 6, **30**

Blue Blanquillo, 106
Blueberry Tree, 71
Bobtail Lizard, 123, 132
boneta, 108
bonita, 108
Boobialla, 71
Booby
    Brown, 104, **111**
    Masked, 104
Borago zeylanica, 98
Bottle-nose Dolphin, 106, 115,
    127
Brachycome, 10, 23, 26, 64
    aff. *cheilocarpa*, **49**, 64, 97
    latisquamea, **90**, 97
Brand, James, 25
bream, 129
    Yellowfin, 129
Bridled Tern, 104, **111**
Broome, 138
Brown, Robert, 23, 63, 66, 68, 93
Brown Booby, 104, **111**
Browse Island, 17, 105
Bruguiera, 16
buccaneer, 4
Buccaneer Archipelago, 142
Bush, Camel, **92**
bush fly, **123**, 133

C

Cacatua sanguinea, 103, **110**
Calandrini, Jean Luis, 65
Calandrinia, 10, 65
    liniflora, 65
    polyandra, 24, **49**, 65

calendar
  Gregorian, xv, 149–150
  Julian, xv, 149–150
Callitris preissii, 2
Camel Bush, **92**
campeachy wood, 3
Camptostemon, 16
Canavalia
  obtusifolia, 96
  rosea, 13, 16, **86**, 96
Candolle, Augustin Pyramus de, 61, 69
Canis lupus dingo, 3, 7, 133
Canterbury, 17
Cape Dampier, 142
Cape Inscription, 8, 12, 139
Cape Petrel, 100, **109**
Caspian Tern, 100
Casuarina, 26
  equisetifolia, 22, 145
Cenchrus setiger, 140
Centropogon, 22, 26, 146
Chelonia mydas, xvi, 7, 12, **119**, 125
Clerodendrum lanceolatum, 24, 147
Clianthus
  dampieri, 94, 143, 149
  formosus, 94, 143
  speciosus, 94
Climbing Daisy, **90**
coastal profiles, 33
cockle, 108, 125
Cod, Potato, **121**
cod-fruit, 15

Coleridge, Samuel Taylor, 135
Collins, J., 26
Colutea, 94
Common Noddy, 104, **112**
conch, 129
Conostylis, 10, 22, 66
  candicans var. *leptophylla*, 66
  stylidioides, 24, **50**, 66
Conus dampierensis, 144
Convolvulus, 96
Conyza, 72
Cook, James, vii, 19, 139
Corella, Little, 103, **110**
Cormorant, Pied, 101
Corvus
  bennettii, 104
  orru, 104
Coryphaena hippurus, 106, **115**
Cottonheads, 66
Court, Arthur, 70
Courtney, Stephen, 18
Crested Tern, 101
Crithmum, 97
  maritimum, 10
Crotalaria cunninghamii, 13, 16, 87, 96
Crow
  Little, 104
  Torresian, 104
Cunningham, Allan, 62, 64, 72
cuttle, 106, **113**
cuttlefish, 108, **117**
Cygnet, vii, xviii, 4, 5, 7, 11, 19, 142, 145
Cygnet Bay, 5, 141, 148

Cygnet Hill, 141
Cygnet Park, 141
Cygnus atratus, 2
Cypress, Rottnest Island, 2
Cystophyllum muricatum, 95
Cystoseira, 22, 28
   trinodis, **83**, 95

D

Daisy, Climbing, **90**
dammar *or* dammara, 63
Dampier, Judith, xviii
Dampier, William, vii
   as hydrographer, 19
   as natural historian, 18
   bird observations, 99
   birth, 3, 145
   court-martial, 17
   death, 18
   early years, 3
   Father of Australian natural
      history, 2
   first Australian landfall, 5
   first Pacific crossing, 4
   in timber trade, 3
   land animal observations, 130
   literary spinoffs, 135
   map of Shark Bay, **33**
   marine animal observations,
      105
   marriage, 4
   memorials, 136
   plant specimens, 2, 21, 24,
      27

   portrait, **29**
   privateering, 4
   second Australian
      landfall, 8
   second circumnavigation, 17
   third circumnavigation, 18
Dampier's English, xvii
Dampier's landing sites, state of
   today, 139
Dampier (HMS), 144
Dampier (town), 140
Dampier Archipelago, 12, 13,
   102, 140
Dampier Botanical District, 141
Dampier Creek, 140
Dampier Downs, 140
Dampier Granitoid Complex, 144
Dampier Hill, 140
Dampier Island, 142
Dampier Land, Dampierland, 141
Dampier Landing, 32, 140
Dampier Limestone, 144
Dampier Peninsula, 5, 6, 141
Dampier Reef, 141
Dampier Road, 141
Dampier Rock, 141
Dampier Spring, 142
Dampier Strait, 142
Dampier Sub-basin, 144
Dampiera, 10, 23, 26, 28, 142
   incana, 23, **51**, 66, 97
Dampiera (streets), 142
Dampieria, 143
Dampierian Province, 130, 141
Dampierosa, 143

Dampierosoma daruma, 143

Dampiers Monument, 141

Daption capense, 100, **109**

Dasyatis brevicaudata, 12, 125

dates, 149

Defence, xix, 7

Defoe, Daniel, 135

Desfontaines, René Louiche, 68

Didiscus elachocarpus, 76

Dillenius, Johann Jacob, 22, 36,
   148

Dingo, 3, 7, **30** (footprints), 133

Dioscorides, Pedanius, 61

Diplolaena, 10, 22, 23, 26, 68
   dampieri, 68, 143
   grandiflora, **52**, 67

Dirk Hartog Island, 8, **32**, 33, **34**,
   35, 130, 139

*Discourse of Trade-winds,
   Breezes, etc.*, 19

Dixson, Sir William, 138

dog-fish, 129

Dolichos roseus, 96

Dolphin Fish, 106, **115**

Dolphin, Bottle-nose, 106, **114**,
   115, 127

Donia formosa, 94

Dorado, 106, **115**

Dorre Island, 12

dove
   Peaceful, 104
   turtle, 104

Dracaena draco, 6, 30, 146

Dragon Tree, 6, 30, 146

Dragons Blood, 6

drawings, 25

Drummond, James, 65

ducks, 102

Dugong, 7, **121**, 126, 149

Dugong dugon, 7, **121**, 126

Duke, xx, 18

Dunal, Michel, 75

Duperreya sericea, 98

Dutch explorers, vii, 2

Dutchess, xx, 18

E

Eagle
   Wedge-tailed, 102
   White-bellied Sea, 102

East Coker, 136

East Indiaman, **31**

East Lewis Island, xv, 12, 13, **35**,
   102, 128, 140

Eastern Reef Heron, 102

Eating Oyster, 125

eclipse of the moon, 16

Eendracht, 139

Egretta sacra, 102

Eliot, T.S., 136

Ellett, Phil, 139

Emery, Garry, 138

emperor fish, 129

Enderby Island, 12, **35**

Endlicher, Stephan, 75

English Rosemary, 72

English travel writers, ix

Epinephelus, 130
   tukula, **121**

Equisetum, 22
Eucalyptus, 3, 16, 24
  calophylla, 3
  dampieri, 6, **30**, 143, 147
Eurybia dampieri, 13, 72
Evelyn, John, 135

F

Fabaceae, 24
Fairy-wren, Black-and-white, 102
fish
  Dampier's figures, **113**, **115**,
    116
  Dolphin, 106, 115
  emperor, 129
  flying, 106, **113**
  monk, 128
  rock, 130
Fisher, George, 8, 17
Flagtail Blanquillo, 106
flathead, 105, **113**, **114**
Fleischmann, Arthur, 138
Flinders, Matthew, 20, 139
fly, bush, **123**, 133
flying fish, 106, **113**
Forrest, John, 64
Forsskål, Pehr, 95
Forster, Johann Georg Adam, 71
Franke, Johann, 69
Frankenia, 68
  laevis, 69
  pauciflora, **53**
  pauciflora var. *pauciflora*, 68
Fregata ariel, 105

Freycinet, Louis de, 13, 132, 140
Frigatebird, Lesser, 105
frogfish, 105
Fucus trinodis, 95
Fusiaphera dampierensis, 144

G

Gaertner, Joseph, 73
galden, 101
Galeocerdo cuvier, **120**, 126
Gannet, Australian, 101
Gardner, Charles, 24, 61, 66, 70,
  73, 146
garfish, 107, 108, 125
Gaudichaud-Beaupré, Charles, 62
Gay, John, 74
Gemmula dampierana, 144
Geopelia striata, 104
Gidley Granophyre, 13
Gill, A., 149
Glycymeris dampierensis, 144
Golden Trevally, 121
Grass
  Birdwood, 140
  Reflexed Panic, 73
Green Birdflower, **87**
Green Turtle, 7, 12, **119**,
  125, 129
Gregorian calendar, xv, 149–150
Gregory XIII, Pope, 149
Grevillea, 24
  pyramidalis, 61
Grey Teal, 102
guano, 131, 132

Gull
  Pacific, 102
  Silver, 102
Gulliver's Travels, 135
gum tree, 3, 30, 148

H

Haematopus longirostris, 102, **109**
Haematoxylum campechianum, 4
Halgania, 10
  littoralis, **90**, 98
Haliaeetus leucogaster, 102
Hannaford, Samuel, 69
Hannafordia, 10, 22, 26, 64, 69
  quadrivalvis, **54**, 69
Hare-wallaby, Banded, **123**, 131, 148
Hartog, Dirk, 3, 12, 139
hawk, 104
hay-cocks, 14
Hemigaleus, 129
Heron, Eastern Reef, 102
Heterodendrum oleifolius, 10
Hibiscus pinonianus, xvi, 97
Hibiscus, Sand, 89
hippopotamus, 126, 149
Historia Muscorum, 148
Historiæ Plantarum, 22, **39, 40**
Hoary Dampiera, 66
Honeyeater, Singing, 102
Hooker, William, 65
Hottentot's houses, 14
Hubbard, Charles, 24, 73, 93
Hughes, Jacob, 16, 133, 147

Humpback Whale, 12, 107, **117**, 127

I

International Code of Botanical Nomenclature, xv
International Code of Zoological Nomenclature, xv
Ipomoea pes-caprae, 13
  subsp. *brasiliensis*, 87, 96

J

Jack Bean, **86**
Jansz, Willem, 139
Jardine, W., 138
jawfish, 105
Jeoly, xix, 136
Julian calendar, xv, 149–150
Jussieu, Adrien de, 62

K

kangaroo, 132
Karrakatta Bay, 5, 6, **30**, 139, 146, 148
King, Phillip Parker, 62, 94, 139, 141, 142
King Sound, 5
kite, 104
Kunth, Carl Sigismund, 65

L

Labracinus, 143

Lagostrophus fasciatus, **123**, 131, 148

Lagrange Bay, 14, **37**, 104, 129, 132, 140, 148

Landing, Dampier, 32, 140

landing sites, state of today, 139

Larus
  novaehollandiae, 102
  pacificus, 102

Lazarides, Michael, 93

Leeuwin, 9, 32

Leionura atun, 129

Lesser Frigatebird, 105

Leucobryum candidum, 149

Lewis Islands, 35

limpet, **122**, 125

limpit, 108, 128, 129

Linnaeus, Carl, 22, 61, 69, 71, 74

Little Corella, 103, **110**

Little Crow, 104

Lizard, 132
  Bobtail, **123**, 132
  Sleepy, 132

Lobel, Matthias de, 68

long tom, 107

Lotus, 10
  coccineus, 70
  cruentus, **55**, 70
  Redflower, 70

M

mackerel, spanish, 106, 116

Macropus eugenii, 2, 132

Macrozamia riedlei, 3

Malacanthus, 106, **113**
  brevirostris, 106
  latovittatus, 106

Malurus leucopterus
  leucopterus, 102

Man of War, 105

manatee, 6, 7, 126

mangroves, 15, 16, **37**

map of Shark Bay, Dampier's, **33**

Marchant, Leslie, 5, 7, 146, 147, 149

Marchant, Neville, 24, 146, 147

Marri, 3

Masefield, John, 138

Masked Booby, 104

Megaptera novaeangliae, 107, **117**

Melaleuca, 6, 16, 28, 63, 71
  cardiophylla, **56**, 71, 75
  lanceolata, 2
  leucadendra, 63
  sprengelioides, 63
  Tangling, 71

Meliphaga virescens, 102

Melville, Ronald, 24

memorials to Dampier, 136

Mermaid, 94

Miller, Philip, 61

Mitchell Library, 138

Moench, Conrad, 72

monk-fish, 128

Monte Bello Islands, 145

moon, eclipse, 16

Morning Glory, Beach, **87**

moss, 148

Mueller, Ferdinand, 23, 64, 66, 69, 71, 93
Mulga, 146
mulla mulla, **88**
Murex pecten, 130
Murray, Thomas, 138
Musca vetustissima, **123**, 133
muscle, 108, 129
mussel, 125
Myoporum, 10, 71
  acuminatum, 71
  insulare, 24, **57**, 71
  montanum, 71
Myrtaceae, 24

N

names
  animal, xv
  place, xv, xvii
  plant, xv
Nasutitermes, 16
Native Willow, 10, 73
Neophoca cinerea, 108, **118**
New Voyage Round the World, 7
Nitraria, 10
  billardierei, 10, **32**, **88**, 97
  schoberi, 97
Nitre Bush, 10, **32**, **88**
noddy, 104
Noddy, Common, 104, **112**
nomenclature of animals, xvi
nomenclature of plants, xvi
North West Cape, 12, 127
Norwood, 17

O

Old Wife, 106, 116, 129
Oldfield, Augustus, 66
Olearia, 13, 22
  axillaris, 72
  'dampieri', **58**, 72
Olive Sea Snake, **121**, 127, 128
One Arm Point, 139
Osbornia, 16
Oxford University, 23
oyster, 34, 108, 128, 129
  Eating, 125
  Pearl, 125
  Rock, 118
  Sydney Rock, 125
Oystercatcher, Pied, 102, **109**

P

Pacific Gull, 102
Pandanus, 6, 30, 146
Paractaenum, 10
  novaehollandiae, **59**, 73
paragood, 130
Parakeelya, 65
parracoot, 129
Patelloida saccharina, **122**
Peaceful Dove, 104
Pearl Oyster, 125
peasecod, 15
Pelamis platurus, 128
Pelecanus conspicillatus, 102
Pelican, Australian, 102
Pelsaert, Francisco, vii, 2, 99, 132

Pepys, Samuel, 135

periwinkle, 108, 125

perriwinkle, 128, 129

Petrel, Cape, 100, 109

Phalacrocorax varius, 101

Phillyrea angustifolia, 73

Pied Cormorant, 101

Pied Oystercatcher, 102, **109**

Pimelea microcephala, 10

Pinctada albina, 125

Pintado, 100

Pipit, Richard's, 102

Piso, Willem, 2, 105

Pittosporum phylliraeoides, 10,
     60, 73, 147

place names, xv, xvii

plant names, xv, 23

     authors of, xvi

     starting date of nomenclature,
          xvi

plant specimens, 27

     summary of Dampier's, 24

Platyaphalus endrachtensis, **114**

Plectrachne danthonioides, 93

Plukenet, Leonard, 2, 22, 23, 24,
     26, 27, **41** (portrait), 62, 63, 64,
     66, 71, 75, 76

Poaceae, 24

Pope Gregory XIII, 149

Porana sericea, 98

postage stamps, 138

Potato Cod, **121**

pouch, marsupial, 132

privateering, 4

Proteaceae, 24

Pseudochromis, 143

Ptilotus, 10, 23, 25

     villosiflorus, 26, **88**, 97

pulse, 15

Q

Queen Triggerfish, 106, **116**

Quokka, 2, 132

R

raccoon, 131, 148

rackoon, 133

Rapuntium, 22, 146

Ray, 23, 106, 108

     Shovelnose, **119**, 125

     Thorny, 12, **118**, 125

Ray, John, 2, 22, **38** (portrait), 63,
     67, 69, 72, 74, 94

Read, John, *see* Reed

Recurvirostra novaehollandiae,
     102, **110**

Redflower Lotus, 70

Red-necked Avocet, 102, **110**

Reed [Read], John, 4, 7, 19, 145

Reflexed Panic Grass, 73

remora, 106, **113**, **114**

Remora remora, 106, 113

Revenge, xviii, 4

Rhagada dampieriana, 144

Rhizophora, 16

Rhizoprionodon, 129

Rhopalorhynchus dampieri, 144

Richard's Pipit, 102

Ricinus, 63, 69

Rime of the Ancient Mariner, 135

Robinson Crusoe, 135

rock fish, 130

Rock Oyster, **118**

  Sydney, 125

Roebuck, vii, xix, 8, 11, 12, 17, 21, 31, 142, 149

Roebuck Bay, 14, 138, 141, 148

Roebuck Bay (ACV), 144

Roebuck Deep, 142

Roebuck Plains, 142

Roebuck Plains (pastoral station), 142

Rogers, Woodes, 18

Rose, Wild, 67

Rosemary, 13, 72

Rosemary Island (Dampier's), xv, 13, 35

Rosmarinus officinalis, 72

Rottnest Island Cypress, 2

Rottnest Island Tea-Tree, 2

Royal Prince, 3

Rudge, Edward, 76

S

Saccostrea, 125

  commercialis, 125

Salural Island, 5

Sammys, 140

samphire, 10, 32, 97

sampier, 9, 10

sanamunda, 63

Sand Hibiscus, **89**

Santalum, 16

sassafras, 9

savannah, 15

Scaevola, 10

  crassifolia, **91**, 98

  holosericea, **91**, 98

  tomentosa, 146

Schlechtendal, Diederich von, 70

Scomberomorus commerson, 106, **116**

Scurvy Coast, 148

scuttle-bone, 108

scuttle-shell, 108, 127

sea cow, 7

Sea Lion, Australian, 108, **118**

sea snake, 126, 127, 128, 130

  Olive, **121**, 127, 128

  Yellow-bellied, 128

seagrass, 147

seaheath, 69

seal, 108

seaperch, 129

sea-pie, 104

seaweed, **83**, 95

Selat Dampier, 142

Selkirk, Alexander, 135

Sepia, 108, **117**

Sepioteuthis, 108

Setonix brachyurus, 2

shark, 106, 108, 125, 126, 128, 129

  angel, 105

  Tiger, **120**, 126

Shark Bay, 8, 19, 125

  Dampier's map, 33

shells, 108, **122**, 125, 129

Sherard, William, 23, 27, 36, 51

ship, sixth rate, 8

Shovelnose Ray, **119**, 125

Sida, 22, 74

  calyxhmenia, 74, **77**

Silver Gull, 102

Singing Honeyeater, 102

Siphonaria, **122**

sixth rate ship, 8

Skate, 12, 108, 125

skipjack, 108

Sleepy Lizard, 132

Slender Suckerfish, **121**

Smooth Stingray, 12

Snake, 133

  Olive Sea, 121, 127, 128

  sea, 126, 127, 130

  Yellow-bellied Sea, 128

snapper, 129

Solanum, 10, 22, 75

  lasiophyllum, **92**, 98

  orbiculatum, 74, **78**, 97

spanish mackerel, 106, **116**

spinifex [*Triodia*], 10, 12, **34**, 93

Spinifex longifolius, 10, **89**, 97

Spinifex, Beach, **89**

Splendrillia dampieria, 144

Sporobolus, 6

Spragge, Edward, 3

Squatina australis, 105

squid, 108

St Allouarn, François, 34

St George, xix, 17

St Michael's Church, 136

stamps, postage, 138

Starry Triggerfish, 106, 129

Sterna

  anaethetus, 104, **111**

  bergii, 101

  caspia, 100

stingray, 125

Stingray, Smooth, 12

Strongylura, 107

Sturt Pea, 13, 35, **36**, **82**, 94, 149

Suckerfish, Slender, **121**

Sula

  dactylatra, 104

  leucogaster, 104, **111**

  serrator, 101

Summerhayes, Victor, 68

Swainsona, 94

  formosa, 94, 143

Swan, Charles, 4

Swan Point, 5, 6

Swift, Jonathan, 135

Sydney Rock Oyster, 125

Synaphea spinulosa, 3

T

Talinum polyandrum, 65

Tammar Wallaby, 2, 132

Tangling Melaleuca, 71

Tasman, Abel, 138

Teal, Grey, 102

Tea-Tree, Rottnest Island, 2

Tephrosia, 70

Terminalia, 16

termites, 16, **37**

Tern
  Bridled, 104, **111**
  Caspian, 100
  Crested, 101
Testudo mydas, xvi
Thornback, 12, 108, 125
Thorny Ray, 12, **118**, 125
Thryptomene, 10, 23, 26, 28, 75
  baeckeacea, 71, 75, **79**
Tiger Shark, **120**, 126
tilefish, 106, **113**
Tiliqua rugosa, **123**, 132
Tomato, Wild, 74
Torresian Crow, 104
Trachymene, 23, 26, 76
  elachocarpa, 12, 76, **80**
tragacanth, 146
travel writers, English, ix
trevally, 108
  Golden, **121**
Triaenodon, 129
Trial, 145
Trichodesma zeylanicum, 13, **92**, 98
Trichodesmium, 107
Triggerfish, 129
  Queen, 106, **116**
  Starry, 106, 129
Triodia, 93, 147
  danthonioides, 10, **81**, 93
  plurinervata, 10, 12, **34**
Triraphis danthonioides, 93
tuna, 106, 108, 116
Tursiops truncatus, 106, **114**, **115**, 127

turtle, 6, 128
  Green, 7, 12, **119**, 125, 129
Turtle Bay, **34**
turtle dove, 104
Tylosurus, 107

U

Uca vocans dampieri, 144
Urogymnus asperrimus, 12, **118**, 125

V

Vlamingh, Willem de, vii, 2, 3, 12, 99, 132
Voyage to New Holland, ii, iv, xv, 17, 26, 105

W

wader, 104
wallaby
  Banded Hare-, **123**, 131, 148
  Tammar, 132
water-snake, 127, 128, 130
Wedge-tailed Eagle, 102
West Lewis Island, **35**
Westringia
  dampieri, 143
Whale, 127
  Humpback, 12, 107, **117**, 127
whelk, 130
White-bellied Sea Eagle, 102
Wild Rose, 67

Wild Tomato, 74
wilk, 129, 130
Willdampia, 22, 28, 143
  formosa, 13, **36**, **82**, 94
Willow, Native, 73
Willughby, Francis, 2, 22, 105
Wirewood, 61
Witsen, Nicolaas, 132
wolf, 132
Woodward, Thomas, 2, 22, 23
wren, Black-and-white Fairy-, 102

Y

Yellow-bellied Sea Snake, 128
Yellowfin Bream, 129

Z

Zamia, 3
Zeewijk, 19
Zuytdorp, vii, 19
Zuytdorp Cliffs, 8